MAN HIGH

MAN HIGH

Lieutenant Colonel David G. Simons (MC)
USAF

With Don A. Schanche

Doubleday & Company, Inc.
Garden City, New York

Library of Congress Catalog Card Number 60–8684

To my parents: Dr. Sam Shirk and Reba Goodman Simons

LIEUTENANT COLONEL DAVID G. SIMONS

MAN HIGH

Chapter I

The Tularosa desert valley of New Mexico is framed on three sides by the towering Sacramento and San Andreas Mountains which drift into Texas and Mexico from the east slope of the Rockies. On all sides, it seems a desolate wilderness stretching interminably to its pine-fringed mountain borders, a bleak canvas on which man has painted some of his greatest achievements. For it was here, on July 16, 1945, that the Los Alamos scientists vaporized a steel tower with an atomic explosion that was to rob man forever of the elusive security he had always sought.

Just to the south of Trinity Site, where the first nuclear explosion was triggered, lies Holloman Air Force Base, and the White Sands Proving Ground from which the United States took its first feeble steps into space. Here the rumbling of rocket motors, the piercing high-pitched scream of jet engines, the cacophonous background noises of the space age became ordinary.

It is a forlorn waste, but across the vast, unfertile expanse there exists a sense of space and grandeur matched only by the deep blue of the sky above which seems to beckon man into the greater cosmic wilderness. Under that sky, in the dust-blasted cinder-block buildings of the Aeromedical Field Laboratory at Holloman, we were answering that call, slowly, tentatively edging upward, away from the earth. And our longest step up was close at hand.

It was an oppressively hot day in August 1955. I was diligently scribbling the flat, dry words of a research study across the spaced lines of a yellow legal scratch pad, racing vigorously to catch up with myself. For two months I had been away from Holloman, launching stratospheric balloons from the quiet and cool lake country of Minnesota. In my absence someone had erected on my desk a cluttered stack of unanswered letters and unread technical journals which I now viewed as a monument to the proposition that I could not squeeze thirty-six hours of work into a twenty-four-hour day.

On the one clear portion of the desk my research report rambled on: "Military Aspects of Observed Biological Effects of Cosmic Ray Particles." The subject seemed absurdly out of place in the austere laboratory building on the flat gray desert. But it was far closer to me than the mass of papers and magazines I had shoved aside to consider later.

For more than two years I had been sending living creatures far above the earth's surface, above virtually all of the atmosphere, to find out what happens to living tissue when subjected to the intense bombardment of cosmic rays from the vast reaches of space. At first, working with a group of pioneering space medical researchers at Holloman, I had helped to launch monkeys to an altitude of 65 miles in old German V-2 rockets. Later, as head of the Space Biology Branch of the Aeromedical Laboratory, I had sent hundreds of animals to altitudes of more than 100,000 feet by balloon.

The military aspects about which I was so blithely writing were profoundly important to the Air Force. Within a few years pilots would have to function, perhaps even fight, far above the earth in an airless void about which we knew very little. One of the greatest mysteries and gravest dangers appeared to be the heavy primary cosmic rays, highly charged nuclear particles raining constantly down on our atmosphere from the space beyond.

I looked up from my work. Across from me, Colonel John Paul Stapp smiled at the cluttered stack of paper that shifted as he leaned against the desk. Then he asked the question that changed my life.

"Do you know enough now to replace your animals with a man?"

It was uttered in a sonorous yet gentle tone, as if he were taking care not to startle me. His brown eyes, behind wide steel-rimmed glasses, were intent and serious and his mouth, no longer smiling, was set firmly above a broad, slightly cleft chin.

"A man, sir?" I jumped up from my chair, forgetting the half-written report and the dozens of other papers that would lay waiting on my desk now for many months more. "I know we can!"

There was no reason to hide my enthusiasm. For months I had been talking and dreaming of the possibilities high-altitude balloons offered as floating research laboratories. With men in them we could observe the stars without the muddying curtain of the atmosphere distorting their images; we could study enormous weather patterns from an observatory far above them; and more important, we could study man himself. As valuable as our animal flights had been, no amount of training will make a scientific observer out of a monkey, although the reverse has sometimes been true.

The Colonel rocked back on his stubby legs and looked first down, then up my thin, six-foot-one-inch frame.

"Is it safe to let a man stay above 100,000 feet for a full day . . . 24 hours?"

I hesitated for a moment.

"Colonel . . . I'm almost certain, but I don't know. All the data we've taken from the animals *indicates* it would be safe. I don't think there would be a danger from cosmic rays. But we still have a lot of unknowns . . ."

"There are always unknowns," snapped Stapp. Then he looked up at me penetratingly, as if I were under a microscope and probed again:

"Would you be afraid to take the flight yourself?"

This, from Stapp, was the key question. And from the intense, level way he asked it, I knew he was not addressing himself to the question of personal bravery or fear. He spoke as a scientist to a scientist. He was asking about confidence, not fear. Did I have enough confidence in the results of my research to become my own research subject? Stapp had taken this step himself and knew its meaning. Studying the effects of high-speed wind blast on the human body, he had strapped himself into a rail-mounted, rocket-driven sled and roared down a track at 632 miles an hour, the fastest man has ever traveled on earth.

"No, sir," I said. "I know I can do it. We'll have to build a bigger balloon, a bigger, sealed gondola. Engineering problems.

"As for the unknowns . . . I'll never know what they are until I go up and face them myself."

"Dr. Simons," said the colonel, now smiling broadly.

"You have just acquired a new space biology program and a new research subject—you!"

Eagerly we sketched out the aims of the flight. My first goal would be to extend our studies of cosmic ray damage to living flesh, only now the flesh would be mine, not that of a mouse or a monkey. I was confident. But I also knew there was a broad belt of ignorance surrounding the knowledge we had gained from the animal flights.

There were no Sputniks or Vanguards or Explorers or Pioneers in space in 1955. The programs to put them there had hardly begun. What we knew of the mysterious cosmic rays was largely conjecture, based on a handful of rocket soundings which had sampled the elements of space for a few minutes at a time, and on our animal flights. Now we were preparing to send a man to the edge of space, where virtually all of the hazards of flight beyond the earth exist.

Only a few years ago, the word "space" to most people simply meant an emptiness between two objects. Today it is a many-layered thing, which needs defining. At this stage in the infancy of the space age our concern is with learning how man can survive and do useful things away from his life-sustaining earth, so the definition should begin with man's needs.

Space begins where the abundance of life-giving gases ends; where atmospheric pressure no longer keeps man's body fluids liquid; and where atmospheric density no longer filters the cruelly penetrating cosmic radiations. The first layer starts at 63,000 feet. Here, man's ability to suck life-giving oxygen into his lungs has long since passed. His body fluids, no longer compressed to liquid density by the weight of the atmosphere, vaporize explosively as if they were thrust into a Bessemer furnace. The next layer of space begins at about 90,000 feet. Here the protective shield of the atmosphere is almost gone. Above this limit, living flesh is almost as vulnerable as if it were a thousand miles removed from the security of the earth's atmosphere. The only security remaining is gravity. Less than 2 per cent of the atmosphere remains to fade away gradually until it disappears entirely at an altitude of 600 miles, where true space begins in every respect.

Our animals—and plants, for we sent radish seeds aloft with the warm-blooded creatures—returned from these near reaches of space apparently unharmed. But it was uncertain work, and we knew the word "apparently" represented a great void. On a few flights we had launched colonies of neurospora, a mold that is a favorite tool of geneticists because it multiplies rapidly and successive generations can be quickly traced. We thought we found definite genetic effects in the mold from cosmic radiation. But there were not enough neurospora flights to give conclusive proof. The only truly positive reaction had been with black mice, whose fur had become peppered and streaked with gray from the destructive collision of cosmic particles with living cells in the hair follicles.

We knew virtually nothing of brain damage. Pathologists performed autopsies on our tiny creatures, shaving paper-thin layers of tissue from the brains and peering intently at the cells to see which of them had been destroyed or forever changed by collision with an atomic particle from cosmic space. It was like searching an unexplored forest for the unknown tree that had been hit by a high-speed bullet fired from the forest's edge. We looked for the trace of torn leaves and broken branches that would lead us to the tree in which the bullet finally stopped.

But except for the gray hairs on the black mice and the mutations that indicated genetic effects in the mold, we never found even the trace. The forest of the brain is still too large for a microscopic survey.

We were uncertain, and we knew it. We were preparing, here in this quiet air-conditioned office with its familiar wooden chairs and steel filing cabinets and wastebaskets and cluttered desks and glass windows and linoleum floors, all fabricated from elements drawn out of the earth and its protective atmosphere, to send a man into an unexplored void at the edge of space.

And I was to be the man.

In the haphazard way that men grow and prepare themselves for the challenges that command their adulthood, I suppose I had been preparing for this role all of my life. But I was never conscious of it in the way of a man who nurtures a goal early, then slips on the spiked shoes of ambition and begins a carefully planned and relentless race down a pre-selected course through life. Such ambitions as I had experienced sped quickly through my conscious mind, carrying with them sufficient momentum to turn me, however slightly, toward the challenges that ultimately would confront me; but although aware of the ambitions and their momentum, I was never aware of the goal until I had grown and lived and the goal found me.

I can remember the influences that propelled me into medicine and into research. Both were contained under the sloping, gabled roof of an old four-story duplex house on Duke Street in Lancaster, Pennsylvania. It was the home of the Simons Medical Clinic: my father, Sam, with his brothers Ike and John, all physicians; and my brother Will, a dentist. There, and in my own house directly across the street, the conversation was always medicine, patients, and medical problems. In both houses on Duke Street there was an assumption which I never questioned: David

Simons would become a physician, too. Until I was much older, almost finished with medical school, the assumption was simply a part of me, like an inherited religion, neither doubted nor zealously pursued.

Behind a dormer window on the fourth floor, in a garret room that smelled of strong chemicals, the Simons Clinic harbored another influence, stronger yet more subtle, plainer, yet more profound, and a whole lot more fun than gastroenteritis and common colds and the Journal of the American Medical Association. As a sixth-grader, I would race to the clinic after school every day, taking the narrow wooden steps to the fourth floor, two at a time. And there beside a battered wooden laboratory bench, I would find Hiram T. Miller. To my eleven-year-old eyes, Hiram was the aged epitome of wisdom, the Mark Twain of Science, a hundred-per-cent genuine laboratory scientist with all the knowledge of the universe at his command.

He was twenty-three years old. Half of each day he spent as a part-time student at Franklin and Marshall College. The other half he worked over urinalyses, stool specimens, and blood counts for the Simons Clinic. But he surpassed the mundane concerns of a laboratory technician in our wide-ranging and wild afternoon adventures in a broader world of science.

"Hiram," I would say. "How will we talk to the men on Mars?"

Neither of us doubted for a moment that there were men on Mars, and that we would one day have to figure out a way to communicate with them. I knew they existed because Hiram already had described to me the extravagant theories of Martian culture propounded by Percival Lowell, the wealthy amateur astronomer who mapped the Martian canals and drew an elaborate picture of life on the Red Planet.

"We'll have to do it with radio, Davie," Hiram would reply, after thoughtfully considering the question. "Atmosphere on Mars probably isn't thick enough to carry sound waves. So they wouldn't hear us even if we yelled. They probably don't have ears, anyway, 'cause they don't need 'em."

"But suppose they don't have any radios?"

"Hm . . . Then maybe we'll do it by mental telepathy."

"What's that?"

"Mind reading, Davie. We'll read each other's thoughts. Won't have to talk at all."

Hiram would muse for a few seconds, and add: "But I'll just bet they have radios. They must know about radio."

Hiram was a licensed ham radio operator, and the thought of a universe without other radio operators was abhorrent. Sometimes on Saturdays, I went behind Hiram's house to a dilapidated barn that had lost the smell of fresh paint before Hiram was born. The inside of the barn was jammed with relics of old motors and machines that had amused Hiram's father, a primitive mechanical genius who would attack a mechanism until he knew every bolt and washer in it, then discard the machine for another one. I would sit enthralled for hours, watching Hiram at his radio, deftly tapping out messages to unseen, unknown, but responsive radio hams thousands of miles away. Slowly, as Hiram explained the theory and mechanism of radio, the exciting mystery of sending messages half a world away disappeared and an abiding interest in radio replaced it. I wanted to be a ham myself. It was the first thing I ever wanted badly enough to work for.

I went to Jefferson Medical School as an Army private

in the wartime Army Specialist Training Program. Despite the heavy load of medical studies, I diligently took time out every week to study international Morse code, ironically at a time when I couldn't use it. Use of amateur radios was banned during the war. But later as an intern at Lancaster Hospital I wangled permission from the authorities to set up my amateur radio station in an unused nurses' dressing room on the top floor. And here, exhausted after twelve hours of effort and study for medicine, I would disappear into a world far removed, and actually do at last the things I had watched Hiram do. After an hour or two at the radio, I would read and study astronomy, another interest Hiram's imaginative mind had inspired.

Then at last I dropped quite by chance into the right place at the right time, and a challenge which combined both electronics and medicine confronted me. I had entered the Air Force as a medical officer, not sure just what I would accomplish by this service, but obliged to do it because of the wartime schooling I had received at Army expense. My first assignment was to the Aeromedical Laboratory at Wright Field in Dayton, Ohio, working with a research group devising electronic instruments for medical use.

One day Dr. James Henry, my project director at Wright Field, matter-of-factly asked me:

"Do you think man will ever get to the moon?"

"Of course," I answered. It seemed as natural to me then, in 1948, as the problem of talking to Martians had seemed when I was eleven years old, but now my knowledge was considerably more exact than the imagination of Hiram T. Miller. Simple engineering progress at the rate we had witnessed it during World War II would give us the means for lunar flight in less than a generation. Carefully he probed again to assure himself that I meant what I said. Emphatically, I repeated my reply.

"I'm glad you answered 'yes,' Dave. If you had said 'no,' I wouldn't ask you to join me." Jim said.

Henry wanted me to go with him to White Sands, New Mexico, where we would launch animals in captured German V-2 rockets. It was man's first effort to send living flesh beyond the earth's atmosphere and define some of the problems we would face in true space flight.

The research group Jim Henry organized was not a large one. It consisted initially of Captain James Henry, First Lieutenant David Simons, and two monkeys. Some other human helpers joined us the night we launched the monkeys. The rocket thundered away beautifully, attesting the care with which the Germans had built it. At an altitude of 36 miles, a fantastic space flight for 1949, the animal capsule separated and was returned to the White Sands desert missile range by parachute. The monkeys were unharmed. One of them is still living quite contentedly at the Washington National Zoo.

Space flight at that time was not a popular subject outside of the comic strips. There was some criticism of Henry's farsighted program, which many people, still not accustomed to jet airplanes, scornfully considered pointless. The critics were not all budgeteers crying over service waste. Some of them were well-informed scientists. Not long before, even Vannevar Bush, respected elder statesman of science and wartime head of defense weapons research, had scoffed before a congressional committee at the "impossible" notion that workable intercontinental ballistic missiles ever would be built.

Ironically, pictures of Jim Henry's mice and monkey experiments that were considered a novelty in 1949 were quite soberly reprinted in magazines and newspapers in 1958 to show that Russia, with its orbiting dog, Laika, was not the only nation that had put animals into space.

In July of 1950, just a few days after the war began, I went to Korea as a newly graduated flight surgeon, but within two years I was back at Wright Field, and later, Holloman, doing research in space medicine. This was the goal for which life had prepared me. I had been propelled unawares to this destination, and I loved it.

Now there was a new challenge: to go at last to the edge of the void which a handful of dedicated men at the School of Aviation Medicine, and at the aeromedical laboratories at Holloman and Wright Field had been trying to penetrate for a decade. Before this program ended it would become a breath-taking adventure, and the lives of five of us involved in it would skip narrowly past the crumbling brink of disaster. But like all adventures in science it began soberly, routinely, with thoughts of hazard far removed.

In fact the prospect of adventure never occurred to me until it was at hand.

We had challenged ourselves to build and fly a space capsule, not simply for the sake of doing it, as a mountain challenges a mountain climber, but for the sake of gathering useful scientific information. There were many things that could be learned by a scientific observer at 100,000 feet that simply could not be discovered on the ground. I knew there would be hazards, but I had enough confidence in the engineering skill of the men who would build the balloon and the capsule to believe that most of the hazard would be eliminated by good design.

The contract for putting the system together went to Winzen Research Inc., a small company in Minneapolis which convinced us it could design and build the sealed capsule and a balloon that would lift one man above 100,000 feet for 24 hours. Otto Winzen, who ran the company, had pioneered upper altitude balloon development and for two years had been alternating with the industrial giant, General Mills, in building and launching my animal research capsules. Winzen brought in the designs by mid-January of 1956. The balloon, whose 200-foot diameter would cover an area as big as Winzen's entire factory, would hold three million cubic feet of helium, enough to lift 1000 pounds to 115,000 feet. The capsule would keep a man alive for 36 hours if necessary. Inside, it would be no larger than a telephone booth. But there would be enough room for enough instruments to make the flight worth while.

As our research program took its first tentative steps, airplanes that would fly as high as the balloons were on the drawing boards. One rocket plane, the North American X-15, would fly far higher, perhaps as much as 100 miles above the earth. The Air Force needed urgently to know such things as how well a man will be able to see above the bulk of the atmosphere. Will the sudden change from the dark sky of space to the brilliant fireball of the sun blind him? For how long?

When the X-15 arches out 100 miles, it will have to come back to earth through the same searing re-entry barrier that a missile or a meteor encounters when it burns hot from the friction of ramming into the dense atmosphere. Can the pilot sight on the horizon to get his critical angle of re-entry exactly right? If the angle is wrong, he may violently incinerate both himself and his ship.

Further in the future, we knew that some day we must attempt to put a man into space, to orbit the earth in a recoverable satellite. Our sealed one-man gondola was really a space cabin, hung from a balloon instead of nestled in the nose of a rocket. With it we could get a realistic idea of both the physical and psychological problems of space flight.

Much of what we know today of man's place in space was then only dimly perceived. Our knowledge abounded in theory based on a paucity of facts. There were countless subtle influences we knew would effect a space pilot, but we did not know what devastating effects to expect. We thought of his lonely vigil in space mostly in terms of familiar claustrophobia, not as the destructive, mind-twisting influence true isolation can be. We had hints from some high-altitude jet pilots that flying high in the atmosphere led to an inexplicable feeling that they had broken away completely from the bonds of earth. Would this breakaway phenomenon affect a man in space? Could it so dangerously distort his judgment that he would no longer care to return?

Ours were not questions of rocket thrusts or pay-load weights or a competitive race with Russia to lift ever heavier objects above the earth. They were questions about man, his mind and his body, fundamentally as old as the first question of the first man who discovered that he was unique among the animals of the earth because he had learned to contemplate himself and ask, "Why?"

To get answers, even to be able to postulate many of the questions, someone had to experience the unknowns where they existed, and return to describe them.

This was what we would do with a balloon at the edge of space.

As the months wore on and the capsule gradually took shape other purely scientific possibilities opened up. We could put a telescope in the gondola and look at the stars as no man has ever seen them from the earth's surface. To earth-bound astronomers the curtain of the atmosphere is like a pane of dirty corrugated glass stuck between their telescope lenses and the stars. The light from even the closest planets, Venus and Mars, bounces and wriggles in their telescopes like soap bubbles in a high wind. With luck we might catch the celestial bodies in a small telescope at 100,000 feet. At least we would learn enough about how to mount and stabilize a telescope under a balloon so that an astronomer could go aloft and study the stars on a later flight.

And I could work on my own research program, to confirm the uncertain theory that cosmic radiation at 100,000 feet is harmless to man.

Although most of our animal research flights had pointed to the conclusion that the effects of cosmic radiation on tissue were negligible, a pioneer cosmic ray researcher in Europe was reaching different conclusions. Dr. Jakob A. G. Eugster of Berne, Switzerland, had sent batches of oat seeds aloft in our capsules and after planting the oats he reported major mutations through three generations.

Even more exotic and somewhat alarming, Eugster excised and dried samples of his own skin and sent them to us to fly in the upper atmosphere. The dried skin was keyed to photographic plates which mapped the exact points on the specimens that were penetrated by cosmic particles. When we returned the exposed skin samples, Eugster reimplanted them on his body. Later, the skin developed dark granules suggesting cancerous growth at the points penetrated by cosmic particles.

There had been no such effect on my live animals. I was eager to prove that Eugster's dried skin simply reacted differently than my own live skin would react. But I had to acknowledge that my eagerness might earn me a batch of minute skin cancers instead of confirmation of my own theory.

We named the program "Project Daedalus" after the character in Greek mythology who built a labyrinth on Crete in which he and his son Icarus, the god of flight, were imprisoned. The father and son escaped from their prison on wax-bound wings; but when Icarus flew too close to the sun, his wings disintegrated, and he fell to his death in the sea. The name of the project fell to its death almost as fast. The Department of Defense sternly warned us to drop Daedalus. Another project already had grabbed the name.

So we called the project "Man High."

As the capsule grew, I spent weeks working with the Winzen engineers, pouring over the minute details of construction. It would have to be as fully equipped with the sustenance of life as the womb. And it was becoming almost as cramped. But we knew that it would work and that it would be roomy enough to be useful as a floating laboratory.

Other weeks went into the careful preparation of elaborate arguments needed to keep the budget-conscious Air Force convinced that Man High was worth the quarter of a million dollars it eventually cost.

Now, with the capsule almost prepared and the plans drawn, it was time to prepare myself for the flight.

Colonel Stapp, who volunteered to be the flight surgeon for Man High, laid out a training schedule that made the prospect of actually flying to 100,000 feet seem anticlimactic.

And he gave me a companion.

On the assumption that we would have to test the balloon system at least once before I took it up for the 24-hour scientific flight, Stapp appointed an alternate pilot to train for the flight with me. The colonel described him as the best jet pilot he had ever known. I had flown with Captain Joseph Kittinger before, and I knew from experience that the colonel's description was, if anything, an understatement.

Chapter II

Joe Kittinger was a jet pilot assigned to Holloman; he was young, with bushy red hair, a strong face that had been played upon by the New Mexico sun until it was freckled like a mud-spattered wall. I first met him in the Fall of 1954. He was laughing with an airman at Base Operations when I walked in wearing my flight suit, ready to go up in a twin-jet, two-seat F-89 Scorpion on a zero-gravity experiment. Joe was to be my pilot.

I knew he had never taken a space doctor up before, so I carefully explained what I wanted.

"One of the weirdest things that will happen to man when he finally gets into space," I began, "is what we call zero gravity, or weightlessness. If he is in orbital flight around the earth, or coasting after rocketing away from the earth at escape speed, he will not feel the pull of gravity. In a ballistic rocket flight or coasting away from the earth in an escaping space ship he'll be weightless, too. Picture an imaginary little man inside a ball that is being tossed high into the air. From the instant that the ball leaves the hand that is accelerating it, both ball, and the little man inside are flying through the air with the same momentum, the same speed. As far as the man is concerned, he is falling. But since the ball is falling, too, he has no support and no sensation of weight because there is nothing to be weighed against. With the slightest shove against the floor, he'll float. If he shoves hard enough he'll bounce against the ceiling.

"We know that some of his organs will tend to float, too, and that could be very bad. The lack of the familiar force of gravity that always pulls on us and everything in us may seriously affect automatic functions you do not consciously control, like the heartbeat and respiration, or digestion, or the sense of orientation. He may not know which end is up.

"When people become weightless for very brief periods, most of them enjoy the sensation. They find it exhilarating.

"But when they are in total darkness and have no visual reference, they may feel like they're falling instead of floating. That's as alarming physically as it is frightening mentally. The body spurts out emergency reactions, like increased adrenalin which speeds the pulse. The feeling of falling might scare the hell out of a man and leave him utterly incapable of action.

"I'm trying to find out more about this feeling by closing my eyes during weightlessness to see whether I feel like I'm floating or falling.

"You can't duplicate zero gravity very long with an airplane, but you can get 30 seconds or so if you know how. The trick is parabolic flight. You dive your jet at a steep angle with full power from about 20,000 feet. When you are just under the Mach limit of the airplane, you pull up into a steep climb and jockey your power so you neither accelerate nor decelerate. The momentum you build up in the dive will throw the airplane like a tossed ball into a high, arching flight path, a parabola. As we go through that arc, we'll be weightless."

"I've done that before for a couple of seconds at a time, just playing around," Joe said. "It's a great feeling."

"If you get the right dive and climb angles, we should be able to get half a minute of weightlessness with your Scorpion," I told him.

"Then let's figure the angles now, before we go up," he said. "The more I know before we go, the more time you'll get."

Kittinger's enthusiasm and eagerness to try something new was impressive for an Air Force pilot. As a flight surgeon, I have found willingness to break with old patterns a novelty among pilots. This is no fault of the pilots, or the Air Force, which trains them to fly by a set of rules for good reason. Experiment and innovation in a disciplined flight group traveling on a mission at supersonic speed could be disastrous. But Kittinger was no ordinary pilot, as I soon learned.

When he had the procedure down pat, we climbed into the Scorpion and he gunned it off the runway with me in the back seat. On the first try, Joe hit the parabola almost on the button, an amazing feat of precision flying for a man who had tried only short, quick parabolas before.

As Kittinger pulled out of the steep dive, I was shoved firmly and tightly into my seat by a pull several times the force of gravity. Then gradually, as the nose of the Scorpion pointed sharply up into the weightless trajectory, the pressure against the seat eased. Slowly a delightful lightness enveloped me, as if I were easing into a buoyantly salted pool of water. This sensation is sometimes described as similar to the belly-tickling feeling of plunging in an elevator or hitting a downdraft in an airplane, but it is not like that at all. A plunging elevator or a plane in a down-draft drop away suddenly, just as you drop when you fall. You instinctively try to hang on to something.

I was easing gently away from the feeling of gravity, slowly becoming weightless. It was like floating in a dream, buoyed by imagination. I had no support, but I was not falling. My arms and legs drifted, tending to float wherever they were aimed. I closed my eyes. Still there was no sensation of falling. Only a feeling of floating, like lolling listlessly in a bathtub, enjoying the body's buoyancy.

I opened my eyes. We were over the top of the arc, plunging downward toward the ground. Now I felt as if I was falling, no longer floating. I longed to feel the leaden pull of three Gs tugging at jowls, arms, and legs, pulling me firmly into the seat. It was the visual cue that had changed the feeling. I wondered how much sight and visual reference effect the sensations of weightlessness when compared to the other senses; the balancing mechanism of the middle ear, the sense of touch, the posture-making positions of deep muscles and tendons? I would make more weightless flights to try to gauge the senses. Other researchers would conduct hundreds of zero-gravity experiments. But we probably would not judge the full effects of this strange feeling until a man rocketed into space and felt them for a long time.

"How was that, Major," Kittinger called over the intercom.

"Okay. In fact it was darned near perfect. I clocked it and you got 28 seconds. Most of the pilots I've done this with are lucky to get 15 seconds on the first run. Now climb up and let's do it again."

"Roger, Doctor . . . And thanks," said Joe.

The second run was as good as the first. Floating awk-

29

MAN HIGH

wardly against my loose seat belt, I reached for the
microphone button.

"This one's perfect, Captain," I called into my helmet
mike. "How do you feel?"

There was no answer. I called again.

Still no answer. Over the back of his seat in front of me
I could see Kittinger's head bobbing.

"Captain, are you all right?"

"No sweat, Major," came the steady reply. "How was
that one?"

"Didn't you hear me call?"

"No," said Joe. "All I heard was a lot of static. Maybe
this zero gravity is doing something to my ears."

"Let's go up and do it again," I called. "It might be your
ears, but I suspect it's the intercom."

The possibility that weightlessness had affected the intercom intrigued me. It was probably a spring switch in
the intercom system overcompensating for zero gravity. As
a dedicated ham operator, I knew the type of circuits in
the Scorpion radio system, and I could not imagine where
the cutoff from weightlessness could be. Possibly in the
mike, I thought. On the other hand, it could be in our
ears, an effect that had gone unnoticed before.

"This time you press your mike switch," I called to
Kittinger, "and start counting. I'll watch my gravity meter
back here and see when the static cuts in." We were completely engrossed by the problem.

He began to count as we arched up in the parabola.
"One—two—three—four——"

I watched the G meter, a small spring scale whose needle
registers a normal one G at rest. Pulling out of a steep dive
it tugs down to two, three, or more Gs. But in the parabola,

it lightened and dropped below one G— .9, .8, .7, .6, .5, .4, .3 . . .

Kittinger counted, "Six—seven—sprffuttg kzrngls . . ."

The gravity needle read .2G when his voice became garbled. As we arched over, I watched it drop to 0.0, absolutely weightless, then start to rise again; .1, .2 . . .

"Sprffuttg kzrngls—ten—nine—eight—seven—six . . ."

"You got garbled at .2G," I called, "and came in clear again when the needle got to .2 on the backside of the parabola. Whatever it is that's cutting out doesn't go haywire until it's almost completely weightless."

"Want to try another?" Kittinger asked.

"Yes. Let's see if we can find out what it is."

"Roger."

We climbed again, 28,000, 29,000, 30,000 feet, and Joe pushed the plane over into another steep dive. Again the radio sputtered. And again we climbed, engrossed in the petty technical problem of a microphone that would not work without gravity.

"Whoa, Doctor," Kittinger called as we began another climb. "We'd better head for home."

"Not enough fuel for another run?" I asked. We had been flying for more than two hours.

"No, sir, we've already cut into the reserve. Barely enough left to get back."

He straightened the big twin-jet interceptor at 30,000 feet on a course that would bring us directly over Holloman. On both sides, the pine-covered mountains surrounding the White Sands desert looked like angry surf about to engulf a quiet, deserted beach. I gazed at them, captivated by the exalting freedom of riding high above these jagged peaks, lifted from their grasp by two powerful jet engines. Above the mountain horizon a light sky, barely tinged with blue, like lightly tinted plate glass, gently darkened to a penetrating deep blue overhead that hinted of the colorless darkness of space beyond, the endless, timeless frontier whose effects on man we had been trying to duplicate in this slower-than-sound, air-breathing war plane. Unconcerned, exhilarated, I was in no hurry to return to the complacent, slow-paced world below.

Captain Kittinger was not so euphoric.

"Major Simons," he called. "I have to ask the tower for emergency landing. We don't have enough fuel in this bird to tool around in a traffic pattern. But we'll make it. No sweat."

At first, it was not alarming. Most jet pilots prefer to land with their fuel tanks close to empty. With reduced weight they can cut their landing speed. And in the rare case of a landing accident, it is better to hit with as little of the volatile JP-4 fuel, a highly refined kerosene, as possible. The lightest spark will set off a raging inferno from which there is little chance of escape.

Barely discernible now at the far corner of the desert was the crisscross pattern of the Holloman runways, still far below and far away. I could feel a slight strain against my lap and shoulder safety straps as Kittinger cut back his power, dropping toward the field.

Suddenly my shoulders and hips pushed tight against the straps. The dive brakes were out and the plane slowed as if it were skidding across a thick glue. Kittinger's head ducked down. He was anxiously working his throttles. Quickly he retracted the air brakes and the plane surged forward again. But the whine of the jets had descended to a rumble. Something was wrong.

"We've lost number two engine." Kittinger's words were quick but matter-of-fact. "Fuel booster pump is out."

I looked at the air-speed indicator. It was steady. The Scorpion still had enough power on one engine to make it. As we dropped toward the crossed runways, the altimeter needles spun like the hands of an outraged clock running backwards.

The radio crackled.

"Holloman tower, this is Air Force 482." Kittinger's calm voice belied emergency, as if he were calling to ask the time of day.

"I'm approaching runway 23 straight in. Double emergency. Over."

A pause. Then an excited voice.

"Air Force 482, I have you in sight. Go around. Repeat. Go around. You cannot land on 23. An F-86 on a low-fuel emergency is landing on 19. Follow him in."

"Sorry, fella. I'm coming straight in. I have lost one engine. Repeat. I have lost one engine. Fuel is low. Repeat. Fuel is low."

"Air Force 482, this is Tower. If you come straight in, you'll cross the approach of the 86. You are on a collision course with the 86. Over."

"Thanks for the information. I'm coming in. Out."

To the right I could see the F-86 Saberjet, also low on fuel, gliding like a hard-flung brick toward the field. Kittinger gently cut back on his failing power. Gradually we dropped. I could see his head turned, his eyes judging the fast approaching F-86. Like a speeding train bursting from a tunnel, the Saberjet grew suddenly from a shining small spot in the sky until it loomed enormously beside us. Then it flicked quickly by, dangerously close overhead. I sighed with relief. The runway was rushing toward us, a safe landing only a few thousand feet away.

A hundred feet above the runway I felt as if we were

safely down. Then the engine whined. Kittinger had shoved on power and was climbing away.

"Damn," he muttered into the intercom. "The landing gear won't come down."

"Holloman tower. This is 482. My gear won't come down. I will try to get around to runway 27. Fuel should get me that far. I'll try to get my gear down on the way."

Joe's head bobbed up and down in front of me. I knew he was feverishly working the emergency landing gear switches, trying to start the hydraulic system that would force the gear down. I looked at the instrument panel. No indication that he was successful.

The Scorpion banked as Kittinger swung around toward the other runway, gently nursing his throttle to preserve the tiny emergency reservoir of fuel that the engine was sucking away. On the ground below I could see three red fire trucks racing toward the runway. They were coming for us.

Turning the crippled jet, Joe lined up the new runway.

A light on the instrument panel flickered, then went off, then flickered again. It was the landing-gear indicator. Maybe the wheels were down, maybe not.

"We'll have to chance it," Kittinger said. His voice still did not betray anxiety or fear. It was serious. But calm.

The jet tilted forward, and I could see the runway coming up to meet us. Fast. But the angle was right. Gradually Kittinger leveled off. Behind the trailing edge of the wing I saw the end of the runway flit by. Then like telephone poles flashing by a car window, I watched the runway markers race past. One . . . two . . . three . . . Then a gentle bump. S-c-r-e-e-c-h. The tires grabbed the concrete. The wheels were down.

Halfway down the two-mile concrete strip, Kittinger let

the jostling Scorpion roll to a stop. Both engines now were dead. It was strangely quiet as he popped open the plexiglass canopy and looked back. Behind the obstruction of his loosened oxygen mask I could see a broad smile.

"Let's leave her here and hitchhike in," he said. "I don't think we have enough fuel to taxi. Even if we did, I'm afraid the gear won't hold up."

The chilling awareness of the Scorpion's triple-emergency landing slowly dimmed. I smiled and a spent feeling of relief spread over me.

"Captain Kittinger," I said. "That was magnificent flying."

"And magnificent luck," he said.

Over coffee in base operations, I studied Kittinger more closely than before the flight. His youthful, freckled face was uncreased by age or worry. There was no indication either in his eyes or his bearing that he had just nursed a faltering jet interceptor through a fast-moving, compounded emergency that would have panicked some older pilots. He nodded to fellow fliers and old friends in the room, but made no move to rush to them with the excited story of his emergency. His hands, as he played with the smooth white end of a burning cigaret, were calm and dry. I had never seen any man so cool and matter-of-fact over a crisis.

Curious, I asked Joe if he was still interested in zero-gravity flights after the nearly disastrous outcome of this one.

"The zero-G parabolas had nothing to do with the emergency, Major," he said. "I honestly enjoyed making the weightless runs. Of course I'm interested in more."

I was delighted. Kittinger was too good to lose in a near accident.

He made many more flights in the year that followed, so many that we accepted him as a member of the scientific team at the lab rather than simply another jet jockey from the air base.

He was a logical alternate for Man High.

With the colonel's support, I had picked still another alternate to train with us. I wanted a scientific observer as well as a test pilot trained for the flight so that we could get full value from it if I was grounded when the balloon was ready to go. Although Joe Kittinger was far more alert and perceptive than any pilot I had known, and grasped the sometimes difficult concepts of science more quickly than most other untrained observers, there was not time to give him the detailed instruction in meteorology, astronomy, and physiology that I knew would be invaluable to the Man High balloonist. I doubt if he wanted to get that technical anyway.

Stapp and I had not decided whether we would need to test fly the system before I took it aloft for a twenty-four-hour scientific flight. If we did need a test flyer, we knew Joe Kittinger would be the best possible man for the job. But for the full-scale flight we had to have a scientist. So we picked another alternate who was competent in meteorology and astronomy and well-versed in physiology and cosmic radiation.

Our training program was carefully planned by Stapp, who wanted to be certain we were thoroughly acquainted with the physical and mental hazards we faced. As flight surgeon on the project, our physical well-being was his responsibility.

First came the critically important test for claustrophobia. Anyone who has felt cooped up in a crowded subway car can imagine our feeling of confinement by multiplying his own a hundredfold. The man who flew the Man High capsule into the hostile upper atmosphere would have to remain bottled up inside a sealed cabin less spacious than a telephone booth for at least twenty-four hours, probably longer. There would be virtually no room for free movement within the capsule, only enough space to stand up in an uncomfortably hunchbacked position, or to sit down in the capsule's springy nylon-net seat.

I was the first to be subjected to this voluntary torture. In addition to testing myself for claustrophobia, I wanted to help Winzen and his engineers solve a problem over how the capsule was to be suspended from the balloon. When Man High was first planned, we were appalled at the thought of making the pilot sit upright for so long, not simply because it would be physically uncomfortable; but because we feared that extreme discomfort would cut so deeply into a man's efficiency that he would not be able to perform the precision tasks required. With this in mind, Winzen designed the system so that the capsule was suspended at an angle, tilting everything to put the pilot in a restful semi-reclining position. But the capsule had to be engineered so that it could be cranked upright for periods when the pilot would be making observations of the sky and stars and the clouds and ground. This involved building a system of cables and motors which would allow the balloon pilot to change the position of the capsule whenever he wished. Unfortunately, the extra batteries necessary to power the system weighed so much that we either had to sacrifice it or be content with not getting the balloon above 100,000 feet. This is a familiar problem to missile makers and is becoming even more familiar to space scientists designing pay loads for orbit or deep-space flight. Frequently the weight of a device such as a television transmitter is not prohibitive. But the weight of its power supply is so high that the whole system has to be thrown out.

Before dropping the comfortable tilting system, I wanted to sit upright for twenty-four hours just to see how uncomfortable it was. At the same time I would find out if I was claustrophobic, an inexplicable nervous reaction to confinement that is shared by many people but recognized by few. Like the dizzying fear of heights, fear of confinement is something which a person can go through life afflicted with but unaware of unless he is subjected to confinement in a degree severe enough to trigger a reaction.

As I stepped into the airliner at Alamogordo, New Mexico, en route to Minneapolis, where the test was scheduled, I felt like a commuter starting his daily run to the office. In the months since Stapp had asked me to head the Man High program, I had been running back and forth between Holloman and Minneapolis at least once a week to work over the endless details of contract, design, and construction.

Winzen, a six-footer with a high Teutonic forehead arching back to a waving line of long blond hair, met me at Wold-Chamberlain Field, a sprawling network of runways rolled out behind the towering Minnesota River bluff at the southern edge of the twin cities of St. Paul and Minneapolis. His small company made its livelihood from commercial plastic bags, the type widely used for packaging supermarket vegetables, but spent most of its effort and, according to Winzen, most of its profits on high-altitude balloon research.

I had known him for more than two years. Winzen had alternated with General Mills in launching and recovering the animal capsules we used in the early cosmic ray studies. And the experience he gained in building the animal capsules had already served well in the design and construction of the Man High capsule.

Otto's engineers had built an aluminum alloy tube, eight feet high and three feet in diameter, capped by pressure-stressed cast-aluminum domes at either end. Around a strong cast-aluminum band connecting the upper dome to the tube were six five-and-a-half-inch glass portholes through which I would observe the earth and sky. Inside the booth-sized tube sat a light aluminum frame strung with nylon net which would serve as a strong, well-ventilated seat.

The company was near the airfield, stretched out in a rambling single-story building behind a tiny lake in which Otto carefully nurtured colonies of rare swans, geese, and ducks. In a secluded room at the back of the plant, his engineers prepared the capsule for my first long confinement.

To be realistic about the discomfort, I donned a hand-fitted Air Force partial-pressure suit, the same one I would wear if we ever made the Man High flight. It is an ungainly thing. Although hand-tailored in every respect, it can become as dreadfully binding as out-of-date underwear, and in places it will pinch as tight as a vise. In order to be worth wearing at all, the suit has to be too small to be comfortable. It is deliberately designed to be just a shade too short from crotch to shoulders. From the shoulders to the wrists, and down the sides of the body and legs run long tubes through which compressed oxygen spurts to inflate the suit and press its life-saving sides against a pilot's vulnerable flesh if he is exposed to fatal stratospheric decompression.

At 100,000 feet, 99 per cent of the atmospheric pressure that keeps our body fluids densely liquid is gone. If the Man High capsule sprung a leak at that altitude, and I were without a partial-pressure suit, my body fluids would vaporize instantly because the liquids, suddenly thrust into a vacuum, would expand into gases. I would literally puff up like a balloon and lose consciousness within twelve seconds.

In an emergency the partial-pressure suit, cramped and uncomfortable as it was, would provide the counter-pressure needed to offset the effects of this vacuum on the body. But regardless of its life-saving purpose, the discomfort remained. The suit stretched doubly tight over the bends of elbows and knees, creating painful pressure points that are tolerable for short periods but become as maddening as persistent torture after ten or twelve hours. A funnel-shaped soft rubber collar serves as a cloying, clammy pressure seal at the neck. Over my head I wore a soft nylon pressure helmet beneath a hard, oversized crash helmet. When closed off with a clear plastic faceplate, the helmet would seal me in an emergency atmosphere of pure oxygen, self-contained within the olive-drab nylon suit.

Like a hunchbacked space man from another planet, I walked stiffly back to the room in which the capsule waited. Because there would be nothing else to do, I took along a light article on Civil War ballooning and material for two long overdue technical reports on the project which I hoped would take my mind off the confining curved walls of the tiny chamber.

Inside the capsule, I settled into the seat, curved aluminum tubes strung with strong nylon woven like fish net, and began reading. It was a fascinating story about Professor Low, "America's One-Man Air Force," who flew reconnaissance balloons for the Union Army and thereby became history's first aerial warrior. But soon I felt a discomforting trickle of perspiration running down my face, soaking the rubber collar at my neck. It was unbearably hot. The room temperature inside the Winzen plant was a comfortable summertime 75 degrees. But in the pressure suit, so tightly molded to my skin that there was no free air circulation, it felt at least 20 degrees hotter. The little body heat that escaped from the pressure suit hung in the capsule, warming it as well as me. The heat left me distraught and irritable.

At first it was simply annoyingly uncomfortable. But as a doctor I knew that it would soon become literally intolerable to my system. Unable to cool itself by normal air circulation across evaporating perspiration, my body would store up the heat and create an artificially induced fever which could be dangerous.

I asked Otto to have the gondola moved outside where it might be cooler. The thousand-pound tube was lowered to a hydraulic lift truck with me inside, fiercely hot and jostling about like a child in an amusement park barrel. Outside I looked over the cool water of Otto's bird sanctuary. It made the capsule seem even hotter. Finally one of Winzen's men turned a garden hose on the outside of the gondola, and the temperature began to drop. But still it was too warm to concentrate on the story. And I had no mental energy to spend thinking about the technical reports I had to write.

I made a mental note. We would have to be careful to keep the capsule air-conditioned well below normal room temperature on the real flight. A pilot assailed by so much discomfort from heat would be incapable of intelligent action at 100,000 feet. Even worse, when the capsule was sealed, his body heat would build up to a fatal fever if the air conditioner did not carry it away.

At last I looked happily out of one of my tiny portholes to see a glittering orange sun shimmer reflectively across the bird pond and drop behind a grove of trees. Now, I thought, this iron maiden will cool off. But it was many hours after sunset before I felt relief.

As the air cooled, another discomfort took hold. My left knee, operated on when I was in medical school, was reacting to a pressure point in the tight-fitting suit. I rubbed it. No relief. I flexed it. Still no relief. I stood up and half turned, trying to kneel in the nylon seat. Still no relief. An hour, two hours, three hours. The pain stayed on, deep, incessant, like a toothache. I craned my neck to look up at the sky, searching for Mars then staring at the bright pin point of orange light that seemed to dance before my eyes. For a moment the pain seemed to abate as I concentrated on the heavens. Concentrate, I thought. Concentrate on anything except my knee.

Minutely I studied every detail of the inside of the capsule. Here we should mount the telescope. What kind of telescope? Five-inch, refractor. Eyepiece will have to be mounted here . . . just so. Radio switch should go here. No, there. Little tape recorder might fit here beside the seat to the right. I'll draw a picture . . . give it to Otto in the morning. Panel camera will go up there. Need to get a picture of the instrument panel every minute during the flight. Need a hook right there in front of me. Got to hang my chest chute there. Can't wear it during the flight. . . .

I dozed fitfully and concentrated again on the capsule; gradually the night sky lightened. Simple brute mental force finally had taken my mind from the painful knee, now down to an aching signal in the mental background like the distracting hum in an ill-tuned radio. I slept.

With sleep and a new day, I was somehow refreshed, as with a second breath. Quickly the morning passed as I turned my attention to the technical reports, details, remembrances of things far removed from my confining capsule. Then it ended—twenty-four hours—time to get out. I had not suffered claustrophobia. I knew I could tolerate a longer stretch in this unique form of space-age solitary confinement. And I knew, too, that the events and chores of a real flight, the need to make dozens of scientific observations, would obscure the discomfort even more than deliberate concentration on trivialities had dimmed the pain of my knee.

Joe Kittinger's test went a step farther toward realism than mine. The capsule was fed with normal air when I sat in it. But Captain Irwin Archibald, an Air Force physiologist who had recently been assigned to Holloman and had already taken on a lion's share of the technical problems of Project Man High, pumped an artificial atmosphere into the capsule for Joe's test. It was a mixture of oxygen, nitrogen, and helium, which we had decided to use for the real high-altitude flight. Arch, a brilliant scientist with the paradoxical appearance of a professional football player, already had tested the mixture for its explosiveness and now wanted to test the effects of the helium in it on a man.

Because the atmosphere had to be highly enriched with oxygen, we had feared the threat of fire which could be touched off by a small spark in the battery-fed electrical system. The addition of helium to the atmosphere reduced the fire danger, but it also did peculiar things to the human voice. As more helium is inhaled, the voice pitch rises. Arch wanted to find out just how far a given amount of helium would shift this voice pitch and how well a man could spontaneously compensate for it by deliberately lowering the pitch of his voice. Joe was the guinea pig.

The more helium Arch added to the atmosphere, the higher Joe's voice rose. It sounded silly to hear Joe squeaking test statements into his microphone in a *vox soprano* influenced by helium. But it was valuable knowledge. In communicating with the ground during the flight, a high-pitched, squeaky voice could easily become unintelligible.

Archibald also ran the temperature of the capsule up to 80 degrees while Joe sat patiently inside. And we got another reaction of value similar to one of my own. As the temperature rose, Joe became resentful and irritable over the tests, even though he had volunteered to have the temperature rise and wanted to see what would happen. Finally he asked us to bring the temperature back down to a comfortable level and leave him alone. I had felt the same sort of irritability when the capsule grew too hot for me. We would have to watch this heat problem. It could be dangerous in many ways. Much later, we found out just how dangerous.

The alternate scientist took his claustrophobia test in a crude imitation of the capsule we had rigged at Holloman. It was nothing more than an old truck seat surrounded by a three-foot aluminum shaft pierced with a few portholes. He wore a partial-pressure suit, as I had. And like me, he sat through the boring twenty-four-hour test irritated, tired, but otherwise apparently unaffected.

Later that night he tried his favorite hobby, weight lifting. He collapsed into bed, utterly exhausted. Two days later, while sitting in his living room listening to the soft tones of a hi-fi set, he passed out. Later, he collapsed again. While driving to Colonel Stapp's house to ask about the curious spells, he became dizzy and very nearly wrecked his car.

Stapp, a long time flight surgeon, was puzzled. The man had all the symptoms of combat fatigue.

Six weeks later, we put him in the test capsule again, this time isolating him completely by blacking out the port-holes. Periodically, he was checked for blood pressure and skin resistance, which would show marked emotionally inspired reactions.

Purposely, we placed the capsule near an open door where the late afternoon sun would hit it. The inside temperature, for a short time, reached 94 degrees. With commendable scientific deliberation, the subject noted both temperature and humidity and determined that the latter made him the most uncomfortable. But paradoxi-cally, he reported disappointment that the temperature had remained high for so short a time. We thought he was eager to go on with the high-temperature discomfort be-cause of an objective scientific desire to test its effects. The next morning we discovered the real reason.

From our side of the capsule the test seemed to be run-ning smoothly during the night. It was almost as tedious to sit idly on the outside as it had been to be confined within the narrow tube. At regular intervals Archibald and I checked with the subject by an intercom phone hookup. He reported the familiar boredom and discomfort from the pressure suit, tedium compounded, but he sounded willing to sit it out as long as necessary. There were no signs of the panicky movement, the panting and restless urgency of action that would indicate acute claustrophobia. The night wore on.

At the end of twenty-four hours we opened the capsule and lifted him out. Laughing over his obvious discomfort, something I had shared in the Minneapolis test, we pulled off his hard-shell helmet and then tugged open the soft nylon pressure suit. Immediately the laughter stopped. The man was as white as cold snow.

Quickly, I lifted his undershirt and placed a stethoscope on his chest. His heartbeat was thready. He was on the verge of a dead faint, in the midst of cardiovascular collapse.

"What's the matter," he said, weakly. "I'm all right. I feel okay. What are you doing?"

I could see what had happened. The man was a genuine claustrophobic, uncontrollably frightened beyond reason by confinement. I doubt if he knew it himself until that test. It was this unawareness that led him to take the extraordinary course he took. He was so highly motivated, so anxious to qualify as a Man High pilot, that he determinedly refused to accept the fact of claustrophobia. Instead of attacking his mind, which was impenetrable, it attacked his body. And despite our constant monitoring, we had no indication of his dangerous physical condition until the test ended.

Without his conscious awareness, it also had made a subtle inroad into his mind. When he had shown disappointment over the end of the heat tests the night before, he may have *thought* he was asking for more heat and discomfort simply out of scientific curiosity. Actually, his subconscious mind was apparently urging him to go the physical limit then and there so that the test and the awful, unrecognized claustrophobia would end. His subconscious was crying "uncle" and he was calling for more.

When the man stepped into the capsule he had already resolved mentally that he was not going to be affected by claustrophobia. This sheer determination never wavered.

Nevertheless, the man's subconscious mind had to find an outlet for the claustrophobia his determination was suppressing. So it began to tear him to pieces physically. Had he remained much longer in the capsule than he did, he would either have had to give in mentally to the fear of confinement or suffer a complete circulatory collapse. In cardiovascular failure, the arterioles, tiny muscular vessels that take blood from the arteries and meter its flow into the capillaries to feed the body's tissues, relax, flooding the capillaries. As a result, blood pools in the capillaries, blood pressure drops drastically, and circulation fails. In effect, a man bleeds to death within his own circulatory system.

Fortunately, we got to him in time to arrest the failure. But he was through as a Man High pilot.

Stapp had been quite firm about our training schedule. After the claustrophobia test we had to experience a simulated altitude of 100,000 feet in a low-pressure chamber. Then we would make at least one parachute jump. And finally we would have to fly a total of sixteen hours in an open-basket free balloon, the minimum requirement for a Civil Aeronautics Administration balloonist's license. We needed a driver's license to drift along the rim of space.

The high-altitude pressure chamber at Wright Air Development Center in Dayton, Ohio is a huge, thick-walled steel tank that looks more like an execution chamber than a scientific tool. If improperly handled it can be every bit as deadly. Once it is clamped shut, strong air pumps suck away its sea-level atmosphere, reducing the pressure inside to that of a near vacuum.

The effects of this vacuum on the human body are frightening. Blood and all other body fluids vaporize violently without a pressure suit to press them as firmly as the weight of the atmosphere does at sea level.

The counterpressure of our tightly fitted, dreadfully uncomfortable pressure suits would protect us. Jet pilots wear the same suit when flying above 50,000 feet to insure against blowing up if their pressurized cabins break open. Normally, when there is a pressure leak in an airplane, the pilot will be protected by the suit long enough to dive his craft to a livable altitude, a few minutes' time at most.

But in the Man High capsule we would not be able to get down so quickly. It would take more than a half hour to descend from 100,000 feet by parachute, and hours to come down by valving gas out of the balloon. So we had to test ourselves and the suit to see if we could withstand a vacuum long enough to get the capsule down by parachute if it sprung a leak or split open in the stratosphere.

I sat patiently while Captain Terry McGuire taped electrocardiograph sensors, tiny dime-sized electrodes, on my chest and back, and strapped a blood-pressure cuff to my arm. McGuire, the father of the rigorous stress tests now used for space pilot selection, would remain outside the chamber and watch the electrocardiograph to see that my heart was not faltering, and the blood pressure to see that I was not suffering cardiovascular failure as the claustrophobia victim had.

Before entering the chamber, I sat for a full hour closed up tightly in the pressure suit breathing pure oxygen. I did this to rid my bloodstream of the nitrogen gas that accumulates in normal breathing. With reduced pressure, nitrogen bubbles can form in restrictive parts of the blood stream and cause the bends, the painful and sometimes fatal malady of divers who rise too quickly from the heavy pressures of the deep.

Finally I entered the chamber and the door slammed with a clang. I could hear a throbbing sound that meant the pumps already were drawing air out of the steel room. As the pressure dropped, I tried a trick which I had learned in years of flying with high altitude pilots. It is a personal tongue-clucking altimeter. If you place your tongue against the roof of your mouth and suck as if to make a clucking sound, you create a partial vacuum, like that of a suction cup. Between 9000 and 10,000 feet altitude, I could create the vacuum more easily, with less pressure between tongue and roof, like resting a suction cup on a flat surface without shoving it down hard. When the chamber pressure reached 20,000 feet, I created the vacuum without even touching my tongue to the roof of my mouth. And at 40,000 feet this effortless, tongue-clucking vacuum was enough to force my mouth open.

As the chamber leveled off at the equivalent of 40,000 feet, I inflated my suit. An airman technician in the chamber checked carefully to see that no pressure points were overlooked. My body was now squeezed tightly inside the suit by a pressure equal to the light but barely livable pressure of 40,000 feet. The airman ducked quickly out through an air lock, slammed the hatch shut, and again the throbbing sound told me I was going up. Soon I was sitting in a partial vacuum equal to the real one at 100,000 feet. The air pressure in the room was only 1 per cent of that we normally feel on earth, less even than a man would feel on Mars.

The inflated pressure suit held the body and its juices firmly in place, but every movement was awkward, performed grotesquely as if I was enveloped in a form-fitting, inflated balloon. I felt a few slight pains from expanded gases inside my digestive tract, but these are experienced by every high-altitude jet pilot. By the end of a half hour, I was certain that I could live in this artificial, suit-enclosed environment long enough to get the Man High capsule down in an emergency. I signaled for an end to the test.

My physical training program was half finished. Next I would try parachute jumping.

Kittinger borrowed the aeromedical lab's venerable old C-47, a World War II relic identical to the long familiar old DC-3 of the airlines, and we flew to El Centro, California, to take our parachute training on a Navy airfield. Colonel Stapp, a master without peer at the old military game of getting things done without delaying in red-tape cluttered official channels, had circumvented the time-consuming formalities of enrolling us in a jump school. Although a U. S. Naval Air Station, El Centro harbors a small group of Air Force men who spend all of their time testing new experimental parachutes. There are no better jumpers in the Air Force, so it was to them that we went to learn.

The leader of the jump group, Chief Warrant Officer Larry Lambert, had worked years before as a sergeant under Stapp. Like most who have worked for the colonel, Lambert idolized the man. And since Stapp had sent us, Lambert took us on like a mandate from God. We got as thorough an indoctrination in one day as any parachutist could get anywhere. Over and over Lambert made us dangle from a rope, swing out over a sand pit, and let go on command, falling blindly to the ground. We did it so many times that before we had finished, our bodies had hit the ground in every conceivable position. And every time he dropped us, Lambert quietly assured us that the shock of a parachute landing would not be half as punishing as this if we would only learn to relax as we fell. We quickly discovered that the more tense our bodies, the greater the chance that something will break.

After listening to Lambert's instructions, I marched to the plane, the same old C-47 Joe and I had flown from Holloman. Joe was piloting, planning to make his jump later. With me were Lambert, to see that I got out of the plane properly, and another experienced jumper who would step out just ahead of me to land nearby in case I had trouble when I hit the ground. Walking to the plane behind us were three other pairs of jumpers; half of them trainees going out as I was behind a seasoned jump mate. As I heaved myself up the ladder to the door of the twin-engined Douglas, I looked ruefully back at the tail. It seemed impossible to me that one could step out the door of an airplane going 130 miles an hour and avoid being smashed against that obstruction.

I sat on a bucket seat clamped to the wall of the plane, leaning forward on my emergency chest parachute with the bulk of the main parachute pack behind me. I dozed as the plane circled the field, waiting for ground recovery teams to get in place for the jump. With a start I awoke, then smiled with satisfaction that I could relax in such an emotionally charged situation.

I watched as the first team of jumpers stepped into nothingness. Unconsciously I waited for the thud of their bodies hitting the tail. Although I knew we would never be allowed to jump if there was even a remote chance of striking the tail, I felt enormous relief now that I had seen positive proof. Slowly I edged toward the open door, staring with fascination and moving closer for a better look as the men ahead of me stepped away. Quickly they faded to small dark specks that suddenly blossomed into white flowers far behind and below the plane.

With the impact of a hammer blow I realized that the man just stepping out was the last one before my jump mate would go. My mate would get a signal, a slap on the butt from the jump master standing at the door. I was to step out right behind him without waiting for a slap on my tensed rump.

Smack! The jump master's hand struck. I hoped desperately that my jump mate would hesitate. Instead he slammed one foot firmly on the step of the door, and a yawning void opened before me. He was gone. Now, me.

It was not a question of courage. If it had been, I doubt that I could have mustered enough to step out. There was nothing out there. To step into nothing, like stepping from a twenty-story building, is unnatural. No man, no matter how well trained, can do it without a qualm. I was wasting time. I couldn't wait for courage. I jumped without it, determined if nothing else to prove I had learned the lessons Lambert taught. I would do everything exactly as I had been told.

Look at the horizon. Feet together. Face down. Count. One thousand one—one thousand two—one thousand three. Where's the horizon? I'm upside down. Pull the rip cord. There goes the chute past my feet. They're not together.

Wham! What hit me? All I can see are spots. Only shock. It's open. I'm floating. Damn. I was supposed to stay right side up. My feet were supposed to be together. I went out like a kid off a diving board. What's in my hand? My Gosh, I did it, I did something right. The D-ring, the rip-cord handle. At least I hung on to it. Lambert said most novices drop it.

Now the sensuous feeling of drifting gently under an enormous white canopy, my best friend. It floated slowly through nothing, like frictionless skis crossing a whipped-cream snowfield. Timorously, I tugged at the risers of the parachute, then I pulled harder. A tug on the right brought a gentle breeze on my face as I slipped away to that side. For five minutes my only link to reality was the gentle, experimental control of the chute and the constant strain of my 180 pounds against the parachute harness. Entranced by the pleasant sensation, I looked down and saw it coming: the earth, rising toward me at 14 feet per second.

Once again. Remember. Watch the horizon. Don't look at the ground. Relax. Relax. Relax as I never have before. Feet together. Knees flexed. Hands up. Don't look down. Relax.

"Take it easy and watch the horizon," a shout from a ground crewman below. "Just relax."

Thud! I'm down. The ground hit me. Too hard. What happened?

Slowly I shook my head. I was stunned. The first moves of arms and legs were tentative. I was intact, and elated.

Later Joe Kittinger went out and came up ebullient, so delighted by the experience that he resolved to jump nine more times to qualify for parachute wings. With characteristic enthusiasm he returned to El Centro several weeks later and qualified. And I returned to the less exciting but vital problems of putting the Man High system together for a flight to the edge of space.

Some of the problems were heartbreaking.

Winzen had finished construction of a full-sized test capsule, down to its atmospheric system, air conditioning, and insulation. Now it had to be tested as realistically as possible.

We already knew that one of the most critical problems I would face when the actual Man High flight came was capsule temperature. On the ground or in an airplane flying through the dense atmosphere of supportable air, the sun's heat and the heat generated by human bodies dissipate naturally. It can radiate or reflect away, just as sunlight is reflected from a mirror. It can be carried away by conduction, which means simply that the heat flows from a hot spot on an object to parts that are not so warm, like water seeking its own level; or more aptly, like heat being conducted by iron from one side of a frying pan to the other. Or it can be carried by convection, the movement of heat by a draft of air.

In the atmosphere, warm bodies transfer their heat to the dense air around them. But at 100,000 feet there would be so little atmosphere that almost no heat would leave my gondola by conduction or convection since there would be virtually no air mass or air movement. Some would leave by radiation, the heat of the sun reflecting away from the shiny aluminum-foil insulation covering the capsule. But there would be no way to dump overboard the heat of my body in the warm daytime hours when the gondola's surface temperature would climb to nearly 200 degrees Fahrenheit.

At night, with no energy from the sun, my body, and the warmed electrical circuits aboard, would be the only sources of heat for the entire gondola. It would have to be thoroughly insulated so that this heat would not escape. If it did, I would be subjected to nighttime temperatures of minus 85 degrees Fahrenheit. So there were two big problems: keeping cool in the daytime, and warm at night.

Some time earlier, the Standards Laboratory at Holloman had hit upon an ingenious idea for a simple air-conditioning unit that amounted to little more than a can of water. Recalling the basic physical principle that water boils at lower temperatures when heated at higher elevations—190 degrees on Pikes Peak as against 210 degrees at sea level—the laboratory calculated the boiling temperature of water at 112,000 feet. At that altitude, water boils at 32 degrees, the temperature of ice.

By placing a container of water in the capsule, we were guaranteed that it would boil at high altitude, even though it was extremely cold, provided it was vented to the outside and thus subject to the near vacuum of the upper stratosphere. Thus, my body heat, blown across the water-can-cooler by a fan, would be picked up by the cold boiling water vapor and carried away. At night I would simply turn off the fan to keep my body heat aboard.

This system and the air-regeneration system which would absorb deadly carbon dioxide, the poisonous residue of breathing, had to be realistically flight-tested. Since we were not prepared to make the first test with a man, we decided to load the capsule with enough black mice and guinea pigs to duplicate a man's heat production, oxygen consumption, and carbon dioxide production.

In October, we prepared to fly the test capsule on the first calm day that came along.

To inflate one of the huge, ungainly polyethylene balloons with sufficient helium to carry a 1000-pound gondola to 100,000 feet is an almost incredibly delicate feat in itself. The .002-inch-thick plastic, so fragile that a child can punch his finger through it, is not as thick as this page. Yet hundreds of yards of it are bound together to make a balloon 200 feet in diameter. When two to three million cubic feet of helium gas are pumped into such a balloon, it stretches to the height of a thirty-story building as it strains against the nylon bands which bind it to its gondola.

During inflation the slightest wind will take the huge

expanse, already straining upward with its lighter-than-air contents, make a sail out of it, and blow it about as if it were tissue paper caught in a hurricane. Ground winds above one or two miles an hour mean disaster for the balloon.

In Crosby, Minnesota, the heart of the great Cuyuna Range iron-mining country, north of Minneapolis, there are a few old and deeply dug open-pit iron mines from which Winzen had launched earlier balloon flights. The protection of the steep canyon walls of the pits reduced the ground-wind problem. But even so we could not launch the fragile plastic bags unless surface winds were below a few miles an hour at the top of the mine, since occasional gusts drifted into the pit.

So we waited for an almost perfectly calm day, confident because past weather records showed at least one calm day every two weeks at Crosby in October.

But the days tumbled over one another as if blown on the gusts of wind that came with them. A week. Three weeks. Now it was November. Still not enough calm for inflation. Should we wait? The wind situation had to get better. The odds said so. Good weather must be just around the corner. Thanksgiving passed. Still we waited. If this dragged out much longer, the growing cost of paying for hotel rooms and meals for the stand-by crew would rob my program of so much money that none would remain to pay for a real Man High flight.

Now it was December. Christmas only two weeks away. We decided to wait only a few more days. If we could not launch the balloon by December 15, we would forget the test and try it again in the Spring. The eleventh, the twelfth, the thirteenth passed. Still not enough calm for the flight.

Then it was the fourteenth, the day before deadline. The surface winds died. Our weather report forecast dead calm between sunset and midnight.

It felt colder than an arctic winter as we began inflating the shimmering plastic balloon under a star bright sky. Shivering in the 20-degrees-below-zero air of the iron pit, Winzen's crew gently stretched the balloon out along a protective canvas carpet and turned the valves that sent compressed helium whistling into the gas bag. Slowly it crept upward hanging perfectly still in the dead-calm air, brilliantly reflecting the crisp light of the moon and the light of automobile headlights that played upon it. At last the cord that anchored the balloon was cut and the capsule swung briskly into the air, rising majestically with its cargo of mice and hamsters.

I followed in a twin-engined Beechcraft, tracking with Winzen's pilot Glenn Hoveland, as the balloon, and its living passengers ascended past the bitter cold tropopause. Unable to see it any longer, we listened to the steady signals automatically broadcast by a radio in the gondola. Steady as a beacon, the radio droned on, giving us signals to indicate the altitude of the precious capsule.

Suddenly the signals blurred alarmingly into static. Then they returned with a tragic change. The balloon was plunging rapidly. It had burst.

After patiently waiting for two months to put the test capsule up, it was coming straight down.

Fortunately the balloon had not ripped completely apart and although its landing was hard, the animals were unharmed. Ironically, they were in more danger of starving or freezing while waiting for us to find them than they were of suffering from impact with the ground. But after crisscrossing the woods from the air, we spotted a blinking red light atop the capsule that showed us where it lay. At dawn we trekked through knee-deep snow into the woods and rescued the animals and our battered capsule.

It was another reminder that no matter how prosaic the gentle floating of free-balloon flight, the giant polyethylene bags do not offer the world's most reliable form of transportation. With so many hundreds of yards of the paper-thin material bound together to form the balloon, it is difficult for an inspector to find every tiny flaw, although Winzen's production people, led by his wife, Vera, did search with extraordinary care for weak points in the polyethylene. One problem with the plastic, apparently the cause of the animal test balloon's bursting, is the cold. At 100 degrees below zero Fahrenheit the polyethylene becomes as brittle as thin glass. This was a danger we had to guard against constantly. It also would be suicide to try flying one of the balloons through a storm. Hail pellets would plow through it like machine-gun bullets.

By March of 1957, most of the research and production problems we had wrestled with for more than a year were licked. The air conditioner and the atmosphere control system worked. We also tested the 40-foot cargo parachute which would let the capsule down if the balloon burst at altitude. Some of the Air Force parachute researchers at Wright Field had been leery of our emergency plans, which called for parachuting the entire gondola system from 100,000 feet if necessary. They thought that in the near vacuum of the stratosphere, a parachute would have no effect at all, and the gondola would fall with such speed that when it did reach the dense atmosphere the opening shock of the parachute would squash the Man High pilot like strawberry jam in the bottom of the capsule.

Otto's design called for the cargo chute to be stretched

open at all times above the gondola, its risers serving as part of the suspension system between capsule and balloon. Thus, if cut loose at high altitude, it would gradually dish in more and more air as it fell, slowing steadily as the air became more dense. There would be no opening shock. On the animal capsule test, Winzen triggered the emergency switch by radio, cutting the capsule free from the balloon at 100,000 feet. An automatic camera pointing upward proved that the parachute worked beautifully.

Joe Kittinger and I, meanwhile, had begun our own balloon flight training. In order to qualify for CAA licenses to fly the Man High balloon, we had to get in a total of 16 hours' flight in an open-basket balloon. Included in the 16 hours were six landings and take-offs, one ascent to more than 10,000 feet, and a solo flight. Because of the extreme scarcity of helium, all of which is tightly controlled and rationed by the U. S. Department of the Interior, we flew together as much as possible during our training, for helium once pumped into a balloon is unrecoverable. We used a Winzen Sky-Car, a small five-foot-diameter open aluminum gondola suspended from a 30-foot-diameter polyethylene balloon.

During World War II, when the Navy was training lighter-than-air pilots to fly its patrol blimps, every fledgling had to check out as a free balloonist. But there was no spare helium, so the Navy used hydrogen, to lift the training balloons. Unfortunately, hydrogen, when mixed with oxygen of the atmosphere, is one of the most explosively combustible gases in existence. It was hydrogen which burned with such tragic consequences when the German dirigible Hindenburg crashed at Lakehurst, New Jersey, before the war. During the war the Navy lost some of its trainees in the same dreadful kind of accident.

When we recalled the hazards ballooning offered in the hydrogen days, our concerns with the dangers of our own system seemed pale in comparison. One of the greatest problems of the old-time balloonists was the frantic task of waving away well-meaning bystanders who rushed up to help when they landed. A lighted cigar within twenty feet of a hydrogen balloon almost invariably meant disaster.

In contrast, we could sit in the basket smoking all we wanted as we drifted idly over the countryside. Once we even planned a cross-country flight on which we would take a kerosene stove for cooking our meals and warming ourselves at night.

Aside from its hazards, free ballooning is one of the most delightful experiences mankind has yet devised. Since man first dreamed, the emotional phantasy of floating and flying has been his most persistent reverie. The Greeks created Icarus and his wax wings. To show how little man has changed in his brief recorded history, all of us still have floating dreams through childhood, and they continue occasionally long after we are familiar with the physics of flight. The psychiatrists say our dreams of floating represent a primitive urge to escape the one binding force we have not yet overcome—gravity. In space flight we will soon get free of gravity's feeling. But in the meantime, free ballooning is the closest we can come to ridding ourselves of the earth's fetters.

A balloon, lacking any kind of power save the lightness of the gas which lifts it, becomes in effect a part of the air through which it moves. As a passenger, you feel no wind on your face, because you are a part of the wind: where it blows, the balloon blows. Without wind whistling by your ears, you are in a strangely silent world, conscious only of the sounds of the countryside below. And you hear the noises of living on earth as you never have heard them before. They are remote, therefore not jarring; you are lifted above them, and therefore are not a part of them, so they come to you like sights and sounds in a dream. I can remember floating gently over Minnesota farms, listening self-consciously to a farm wife singing as she worked in her kitchen, to another scolding her husband. Curiously, the only creatures who ever seemed aware of the balloon drifting by were the chickens. Other farm animals would remain blithely ignorant of our presence above, but chickens always sensed it, looked up, and cackled wildly. Instinctively alert to the dreaded chicken hawk, they must have looked upon a balloon as the granddaddy of all predators.

On one flight near Holloman with Joe and our project meteorologist, Duke Gildenberg, we drifted gently about 50 feet above the ground for two hours, following the winding course of a dry river bed, turning where it turned, bobbing and floating above it as water had bobbed and churned in it years ago. In the early morning calm, the cool air was imperceptibly draining down the course of the old creek, and we were flowing with this slow river of air. Below us an occasional jack rabbit would twitch his nose and flick his ears, oblivious of our presence until one of us shouted directly overhead. Then he would race away, zigzagging wildly because he could not decide where safety lay.

I had finished my training by this time in the spring of 1957 and was riding as an instructor for Joe and Duke. As we drifted along the dry bed, they took turns practicing light touchdown landings and take-offs. To land they would valve a little gas, reducing the balloon's lift. When the basket touched the ground, they would spill a small handful of ballast, cutting the weight of passengers and equipment enough to allow the remaining gas to lift us again.

Later in the day, the morning calm had passed; and we faced a stiff 15-mile-an-hour breeze on the ground. It got us into serious trouble. On a few previous touchdowns we had struck the hot desert uncomfortably hard. So the three of us decided to stand for the next landing so our flexed knees could take up the shock of hitting the ground. We forgot to take account of the ground wind, which was giving us forward speed. As the gondola struck, all of us pitched forward in the basket. I slammed violently into Duke Gildenberg, pressing him between my chest and the rail of the gondola. As we rose into the air again, he slumped to the floor, gasping for breath. I had fractured one of his ribs.

Ballooning was not all idyllic drifting over pastoral scenery.

Chapter III

"The polyethylene balloon," said Duke Gildenberg, "is nothing but a rather profoundly engineered vegetable bag, with one very important difference. If you want to know how many pounds of potatoes a plastic bag will hold, you simply start shoving in potatoes. But there is no way to dynamically test a balloon without ruining it. You just have to trust that the people who put it together have looked over every square inch of the polyethylene and found no flaws."

We were in my office at the Aeromedical Field Lab at Holloman. Duke, a shy, thin bachelor who had chased hundreds of research balloons across the United States in ten years as an Air Force meteorologist, rocked his chair back against the scarred wall of the room and looked at Colonel Stapp, who was standing by the window.

"I know the balloon can't be tested," said the colonel. "But the capsule can."

"It has been tested," I reminded him, "six times. We know that the atmosphere system works, the parachute recovery system works, and the power system works. We've recovered animals unharmed after every flight. With the exception of the first test flight, when the balloon burst, every one of them has gone off without a hitch."

"Animal tests are fine, Dave, but I don't think that's enough." Stapp strode to my desk and continued:

"The animals did nothing up there but breathe, eat, and defecate. They didn't talk on the radio or shift around in a 180-pound mass or fidget in a pressure suit or try to grab scientific observations out of those saucer-sized portholes, or do any of the things you will have to do when you go up.

"To put the Man High system up now for a full-scale flight without at least one manned test flight first would be like trying to send a new fighter plane into combat without wringing the bugs out of it."

I cradled my forehead in a cupped hand and sighed. The idea of a test flight was a good one, probably essential. But I had been hoping we could get by without it. As project director, I was responsible for the funds for the flight. And we simply could not afford it.

Over a year before when Stapp first proposed Man High, we battled furiously for the money to get started. It was almost as hard as drawing water from a dry well. The money came in small driblets: a little for the first feasibility study by Winzen Research; a little more for construction of the gondola; then a slow and unsteady trickle of funds to pay for the animal test flights and the travel which ate steadily away at my budget as I commuted between Holloman, Minneapolis, and Wright Field.

At one point the well ran completely dry. To rescue me Stapp diverted funds to Man High from his own rocket-sled program, then both of us went begging. At each stage we had to besiege headquarters of the Air Research and Development Command in Baltimore with new arguments for money. But ARDC was faced with the same problem on a much grander scale to get money for vital missile and aircraft programs as well as for smaller research efforts like ours. Short of cash for established and priority programs, they were rightfully wary of non-essential efforts. And Man High was so low on ARDC's list of essential programs that I was afraid we would be turned down flatly if we asked for money again. It looked to me as if the manned test flight was a painful necessity, so painful that the whole program would fold up because of it.

"If we do have a test flight, Colonel, we will be absolutely broke when it's over. Do you think we can count on more money from ARDC to make the full-scale flight?" I was unwilling to give in, and Stapp knew it.

"You can't count on finding more money," he said bluntly. "But I'd rather see you take a chance on getting more money after a test flight than take a chance on flying without a test. If you took that system up now and anything at all went wrong, Man High would be as dead as yesterday's news. Suppose the capsule springs a leak on your ascent and you have to come right down without even getting to altitude? Could you get the money to patch things up and try again? It will be a lot easier to justify paying for a normal test flight, something which the Air Force is accustomed to, than it will be to justify repeating a failure."

"I wish our ability to get money was as unassailable as your logic, Colonel," I smiled ruefully. "You're right about the test flight, of course. But I'd give anything for assurance that we won't run into a brick wall when we go back for the funds for the big flight."

"I don't think headquarters will hold you down just when

65

you're ready to go," mused Stapp. "Not unless we do something that makes them think they would be throwing good money after bad. A sensible test flight should convince them it's good."

"If the system works all right maybe we can get some scientific value out of the test hop," I suggested, hopefully. "If I fly the test myself, I should be able to get some sky-brightness readings. It will have to be a short flight, not more than eight hours. But in that time I can at least check the stability of the capsule so we'll know whether the telescope will work on the long flight."

Colonel Stapp turned toward the window, his hands clasped behind his back. From his awkward silence, I knew he was carefully framing his next words. With a sinking awareness, I knew what he would say.

"I want Kittinger to make the test flight," he said. "I've already talked to him." Stapp paused, removed his glasses, then continued in a subdued, mild tone.

"Dave, as a flight surgeon and as your boss, I'm responsible for the physical well-being of everyone who gets into that capsule as well as for seeing that the program arrives at its goal. The goal is your 24-hour scientific flight. I will be the flight surgeon on the ground, but I have had no experience with tracking and recovery of balloons, and I think I need you to check me out in these things before you go up. Besides, if you tested the capsule and had even a mild accident, it might put you out of action altogether and that would be the end of Man High. I can't let you go. You're a doctor, not a test pilot."

Again his logic was unassailable. I was annoyed at the nagging tug of vanity I felt, the reluctance to move aside for another Man High pilot. The months of preparation had left me so thoroughly accustomed to the notion that

66

I would be first to pilot the Man High capsule that the idea was hard for me to surrender now, even though I knew perfectly well that we had trained Kittinger for just such a possibility.

There was no question that he was qualified to test the system. As a jet pilot he had acquired experience in functioning alone and intelligently in aerial emergencies, an experience for which I had been thankful on at least one occasion. I wanted to do it myself. But I wanted much more to get something of scientific value when I went aloft. And I knew that even if I made the short test flight it would not have much scientific value.

My voice probably betrayed an effort to sound more enthusiastic than I felt as I acknowledged the common sense of the colonel's decision.

"I'll have to finish checking Joe out as a balloon pilot," I said. "Then we can go ahead."

Stapp smiled, clearly showing grateful relief. The issue was settled.

"When can you have the system ready to launch?" he asked.

"Probably around the first of June," I answered, "providing the weather is with us." I looked questioningly at Duke Gildenberg, still sitting quietly with his chair propped against the wall.

In all of my experience, I have never known a more uncannily accurate weather forecaster. At Holloman, his prowess is legendary. I remember once watching him on a parachute test program in which a balloon was to be floated to 90,000 feet, where an automatic device would cut loose a dummy wearing a new test parachute. The men running the program wanted to know where to station themselves to retrieve the dummy. Duke checked his weather charts and telephoned for information on surface winds. Then he quickly figured the course that the balloon would take as it drifted first east, then north, then west, and finally southeast on a speeding jet stream.

"As soon as you've launched the balloon, you come over here to the command post and stick with me," he told the parachute researchers. "I'll take you to within a hundred yards of it."

After the launching, the puzzled testers waited restlessly with Duke, wondering when he was going to leave for the recovery point. As the minutes ticked anxiously by, Duke calmly studied a map. Finally he looked at his watch to see that the parachute had been cut loose. Then he ambled nonchalantly to a window and looked out. The flabbergasted testers followed, just in time to see their parachute-borne dummy drop less than 100 yards away.

If Duke Gildenberg looked up at a clear summertime sky above the Sahara desert and said it would snow within five minutes, I would start looking for a pair of snowshoes.

"Early June should be perfect in Minnesota," Duke said. "Winds in the stratosphere will have shifted from eastward to westward by then. If you launch the flight from Minneapolis it shouldn't drift very far away. And the ground winds there are good for launching at that time of the year."

I told ARDC and Winzen that we wanted to start getting things ready for the test flight, then left for Minneapolis with Archibald and Joe Kittinger.

As soon as we arrived Joe eagerly began soaking up all the information he could get about the capsule. For hours on end he would sit inside its uncovered framework checking the location of switches and popping questions at Winzen's chief engineer, Don Foster.

"What do I do if the capsule starts to lose pressure?"

"Check for leaks at the windows first," Foster's laconic voice would reply, "then check for a leak in the main seal where the lower shell is clamped to the capsule turret. If you're still losing pressure, turn the oxygen-regulator valve to 'manual' and start dumping oxygen into the capsule to get the pressure up."

Kittinger would pause, memorizing the procedure, then shoot another question.

"What do I do if the leak continues and I have to go on emergency oxygen?"

"Clamp the faceplate on your pressure suit and start drawing oxygen from the emergency suit supply. If pressure drops real fast, inflate the suit and cut the capsule loose from the balloon. The main cargo chute will let you down slow enough so you won't get hurt when you hit the ground."

"How fast does the cargo chute come down?"

"It'll take at least half an hour from 100,000 feet. When the capsule hits the ground it'll be going about 30 feet per second. That's about 20 miles an hour."

"Wouldn't I land softer if I dropped out of the capsule and used my own chute?"

"Probably, but you'd stand a much greater chance of getting hurt. The capsule is built with a collapsible tubular-frame undercarriage that's designed to take up the landing impact. If you hit in the water, the capsule will float until someone reaches you."

Day after day, Kittinger sat in the capsule studying its layout, and more and more his interest seemed to settle on the emergency procedure for bailing out. He was most curious, I thought, about the possibilities of escaping from the capsule, bodily bailing out of the thing, from 100,000 feet. No one had done this before. And no one knew for sure what would happen to a man who did. But we had a pretty good idea. If a man bailed out at 100,000 feet, into the virtual vacuum there, his partial-pressure suit would protect his body juices, but he would need an electrically warmed suit of some kind to keep from freezing to death. If he pulled his rip cord right away, his parachute most likely would fail to open. If he delayed opening the chute he probably would lose consciousness, or perhaps be spun to death by the aerodynamic instability of his own body. Even if he did remain conscious in a free fall to 20,000 feet or so, when he did pull the rip cord, the shock of the chute's opening probably would snap him in half.

Parachute testers had dropped dummies from 90,000 feet. But the data from the dummies made survival seem impossible. Most flight surgeons familiar with parachute injuries and the terrific strains that would result from a body's wild spinning through airless space were convinced that a 90,000-foot bail-out would be a suicidal mistake.

But now our own test pilot, Joe Kittinger, showed signs of contemplating such a jump himself. I remembered the ebullience he had shown after his first parachute jump, and the intense preoccupation with returning to El Centro for more jump training. He relished the delightful experience of parachute jumping so much that Stapp and I feared his preoccupation with jumping would leave him eager to find an excuse to bail out of the capsule. Neither of us knew for sure whether Kittinger would live through such an experience. But we were dead certain that the Man High program would not survive it.

If he bailed out, it probably would cost us the capsule. In order to jump, the lower half of the capsule containing power supply and air-regeneration equipment would have to be jettisoned. Even if we could find it, the jettisoned section would be nothing but a crumpled mass of aluminum.

Stapp called Kittinger into Otto Winzen's glass-enclosed office. And together we laid down the law.

"There is one and only one emergency that calls for such a drastic step," I said. "That is an uncontrollable fire. If there is a fire in the gondola, and it's too much for your small extinguisher, you will have to get out. Otherwise, regardless of what happens, stay with the capsule. If it loses pressure, you have a pressure suit and emergency oxygen that will last long enough for you to come down by the capsule cargo chute.

"There's a remote possibility that some emergency we haven't thought of will force you to bail out of the capsule. But you positively must not do it unless you are under 30,000 feet. Even then, don't do it unless you absolutely have to. The capsule is the best protection you can get if you pile into trees or water."

Kittinger left the office somewhat chastened, but convincingly agreeable over the folly of a bail-out. Still I was haunted by the possibility that he might try it.

Until this point, just a few days before the test flight, my admiration for Joe Kittinger had been unbounded. Now it was beginning to pale. Was it my own vanity? A bruised ego still reluctant to concede first place to another pilot? Or did I detect an ambitious aggressiveness in Joe that threatened more than vanity?

Until the question of Kittinger's test flight was raised, I had not realized how completely jealous of the Man High program I had become. Practically every minute of my time, from the first day the project was proposed by Stapp, a year and a half before, had been devoted to it.

I knew almost from the beginning that I might have to step aside to make room for another pilot before I flew. I had even convinced myself that I would willingly step aside if it was necessary. We had trained Joe specifically to be a test pilot. And the test flight certainly was necessary, with Joe clearly qualified. Yet I was becoming more and more reluctant to see him take it. Difficult as it is to be completely objective with oneself, I tried, and slowly I perceived the source of my disenchantment and my growing fear of Kittinger.

His motives for wanting to fly the Man High balloon into this exotic and hostile realm where no man had been before were pure, but they differed from my own. Joe quite frankly acknowledged that to him the flight was a mixture of a sporting and professional challenge as an aviator. He wanted to be the first man to do it if for no other reason than to prove that it could be done. He wanted to be the first to see what it was like to float along the rim of the atmosphere.

I had some of the same motivation—the desire to be first just for the sake of being first—but I was trying to swallow it for the sake of an orderly research program. A much more powerful motive for my desire to fly the capsule was the purely scientific urge to go into unexplored territory to study it. I was far more interested in the frontier than the covered wagon that would take me there. The Man High system as I saw it was primarily a laboratory, one in which I could conduct experiments that would be impossible in any other laboratory. I looked upon myself as little more than an integral part of this complicated scientific machine.

The wariness I was beginning to feel for Joe clearly was due to a growing realization that his test flight could destroy the scientific apparatus I had spent a year and a half helping to devise and planning to fly.

I was afraid that he might accidentally or impetuously squeeze me out of my own research program. When boiled down to that single source, the fear seemed groundless. Still I could not get it out of my mind. Nor could I convince myself that Kittinger had abandoned his urge to use the Man High capsule for a parachute test.

The day of Joe's flight was drawing close. We had scheduled it for June 2, a day which the omniscient Duke Gildenberg forecast would be perfect for ballooning. Duke's forecast was so optimistic, in fact, that we decided to make the launch from a prairie-flat airfield not far from Winzen's plant rather than trail through the north woods to the deep and rugged iron pit at Crosby. The balloon and launching equipment were trucked to Fleming Field, the nearby airport, and on the night of June 1 we began to prepare for man's first assault on near space.

Colonel Stapp and I carefully checked Joe's pulse, blood pressure, and respiration before he began squeezing into the tight and uncomfortable pressure suit. As one of the first steps, before zipping the sweltering suit shut, Archibald taped a tiny microphone to his chest, just over his heart. The mike would be connected later to a lead wire from the capsule's low-frequency radio. From it we would be able to listen whenever we wished to a beeping sound that told his heartbeat, and to the rasping of his breath. The information would not be as complete as we would get from a patient in an examining room, but it would tell us generally how Joe's body was standing up to the rigors of the flight. If there were any alarming changes in his heartbeat or respiration, we could order him down.

If for any reason he lost consciousness before he could

start the balloon's descent, we could cut him down remotely by a radio-controlled switch that would separate the balloon from the gondola and bring the system down by cargo parachute.

This remote cut-down system had given both Joe and me some cause for alarm. Neither of us particularly liked the idea of hanging in space at the whim of someone on the ground. A mistake at the ground control switch could end the flight without giving the pilot a chance to argue. Even worse, there was a slim possibility that a misguided radio signal from some outside source like a ham radio station could trigger the cut-down switch. I ruefully remembered one balloon flight at Holloman which was accidentally cut down when the jarring tones of "Tiger Rag," played by a local disc jockey, coincidentally formed the coded signal necessary to trigger the remote switch.

Kittinger, hunchbacked in the cramping suit, walked stiffly to the gondola room of the Winzen plant and climbed into the nylon-net seat which occupied most of the space inside the capsule frame. The framework, with the dome-shaped hemisphere attached to it, was perched on a wooden platform under a small crane. When we were ready to seal the capsule, the crane would lift Kittinger together with the frame, then let it down inside the aluminum tube of the capsule, like slipping a knife into a sheath. Strong ring clamps at the top of the sheath connected tightly with the hemispherical dome that capped the framework.

At 1 A.M. the crane lifted Joe and frame. The lower section of the gondola was rolled underneath, and Joe was dropped inside the confining walls. He would not emerge until the flight ended. Methodically, Archibald flushed away the normal air trapped in the capsule when it was sealed, and regulated the flow of a new atmosphere better suited to space flight. It contained 60 per cent oxygen as opposed to the 20 per cent we normally breathe. Nitrogen was limited to 20 per cent rather than the normal 79 per cent to reduce the chances of bends. And the remainder of the atmosphere was helium, which is almost entirely absent from the air we breathe. Helium, an inert gas, was used to replace normal nitrogen as well as to damp out the chances of fire in the oxygen-rich air.

As Arch checked the capsule pressure, I walked over to a drafting table where Duke Gildenberg was sitting quietly, drumming a monotonous signal with the end of a pencil.

We listened as Archibald and Kittinger talked over an intercom system connected to a loud-speaker. At first Joe's voice rose to a high squeak when Arch added the helium to his atmosphere. Then gradually it fell to almost its normal pitch. He was consciously compensating for the high pitch the light air gave to his vocal cords.

So far everything was running as planned.

"Duke, if your forecast holds up and we get this flight off on schedule I'll be flabbergasted," I said, recalling with pain the two idle months spent waiting for good weather at Crosby when we launched the first test capsule.

"It will, and you will," said Duke, dryly. "Betting on weather forecasts is not very profitable, but I would be willing to bet on this one."

"If you're willing to put money on it, it must be a cinch. Whenever you're that confident, I know you must be right."

"Want to bet?"

"No thanks. Let's do it sometime when you're not so positive," I laughed. If Gildenberg bet the weather would be perfect, I knew it would be perfect.

For the next two hours I buried myself in the details

of the final checkout. By 4 A.M., with everything in order, we were ready to go.

With Joe jostling about inside, the capsule was shifted to a pickup truck to be driven to Fleming Field, ten miles away. It seemed like a cruel form of torture to seal Kittinger in so many hours before the scheduled dawn launch, but it was necessary. By breathing the unusual capsule atmosphere for several hours, his body had a chance to rid itself of the large quantity of nitrogen absorbed in normal breathing. By dawn he would be completely accustomed to the strange climate and, more important, if the capsule burst as he ascended there would be too little nitrogen in his blood stream to form bubbles and cause the bends.

The capsule had the appearance of an extraordinary icebox as we trailed its truck along the roads south of St. Paul toward Fleming Field. The domed top had been carefully packed with dry ice which was now fuming against the dark sky. Although seemingly crude, the dry ice packing was an effective coolant for the hermetically sealed capsule, whose air-conditioning system would work only at high altitudes where its frigid water would boil away in the rarefied atmosphere.

On the narrow runway of the tiny airfield ground fog hung just above the heads of the balloon-launching crew. They had stretched the huge polyethylene balloon along its canvas carpet, clamping the end that would swell first with gas into a mechanical launching arm. Efficiently the crew moved into action, a routine that had become almost automatic in years of launching research balloons. The launchers coupled hoses to two tank trucks filled with compressed helium, then turned the valves that sent the high pressure gas screeching into plastic tubes feeding into the main gas bag. Slowly the balloon lifted, taking on a bubble shape at the top where the helium strained upward against it.

Some of the early morning airport workers who stood by the runway watching the weird proceedings wondered why we did not fill the bag completely with helium, bringing the giant balloon out to its full spherical shape. The reason was quite simple. Two million cubic feet of helium at sea level expand to 200 million cubic feet at the near vacuum of 100,000 feet. A balloon that starts out only 1 per cent full on the ground will swell to its full size as it rises into the stratosphere. If it is overinflated on the ground, the gas will swell at altitude until it squeezes out of the open neck of the balloon to be lost in space. Even at the government price of three cents a cubic foot, helium is too precious to waste that foolishly.

Overhead our faithful old C-47 from Holloman droned by. Inside it were Captain Hank Fronkier, the pilot, and Captain Drury Parks, a zoologist from my space biology lab at Holloman who was overseeing the aerial tracking of the balloon. At times it is extraordinarily difficult to keep track of high-altitude balloons even when they are in constant radio contact. The balloon pilot, even with so much of the earth visible below him, is usually too busy to know exactly where he is. And if haze or a cloud layer comes between the ground crew and the balloon, it can become completely lost in the stratosphere.

But on a clear day a balloon as large as Kittinger's is easily visible to the naked eye. The shining, ball-shaped 172-foot balloons are so visible, in fact, that it is sometimes amusing to track them by way of the flying saucer reports that follow in their wake. One long-lasting balloon launched from Holloman in October of 1953 showed up over England about a week later after it had been lost to visual tracking in the United States. The trackers found it by following press reports of a flying saucer that was variously described as having "tremendous speed," being "practically motionless," and "reflecting a fierce light." The fact that British radar stations also spotted the strange object convinced flying-saucer enthusiasts that they had finally bagged a real one. Regrettably, the U. S. Air Force had to announce that what the saucer lovers were watching was Holloman Balloon Flight Number 175.

The Winzen company, whose contract with the Air Force gave them complete responsibility for launching, tracking, and recovering the balloon, had a small Navion light plane standing by with Glenn Hoveland, an experienced balloon tracker, as the pilot. Near the Navion were two helicopters, one of them for use by Stapp, Technical Sergeant Edward Dittmer, and me as a tracking and medical emergency crew, and the other to ferry Otto Winzen, his wife Vera, Captain Archibald, and others of the crew from Fleming back to the Winzen Plant where the central radio command system was located.

I looked at the gleaming capsule as it sat waiting to be pulled into the stratosphere. It was completely wrapped in aluminum-coated mylar film and sparkled brightly in the dim predawn light as automobile headlights and the beams of flashlights sprayed across it. Under the glistening covering, four quarter-inch layers of honeycombed paper fiber served like the airspace in a vacuum bottle to insulate the capsule. Ed Lewis, a field-toughened meteorologist who was working as Winzen's launch chief, directed one of the final pre-launch steps: attaching the six nylon suspension lines of the gondola to the risers of the cargo parachute.

The chute in turn was attached to a suspension harness at the base of the balloon.

Launch was only moments away.

During the night of preparation I had been so busy checking Kittinger's well-being, briefing the tracking crew, and helping to check out the gondola system that I had not had time to reflect on the enormity of the adventure. Now I stood quietly at the sidelines during the last moments of preparation, little remaining to do until Joe was on his way. The shaded orange rays of the rising sun were beginning to play across the shimmering plastic balloon which now rose high in the dead morning calm. I could not suppress an excited shiver as I realized that Man High at last was ready to fly. The excitement of seeing the capsule, sealed as tight as a beer can with a space-destined man inside, far outweighed the mild disappointment I still felt over the fact that another man was taking it up. If Kittinger made no mistakes I knew it would fly and the test would succeed. But my emotions were as mixed as those of a mother watching her favorite child playing with a valuable vase. If anything happened to make the test a failure, the Man High program and my chances of ever getting this compact laboratory to the unexplored edge of space would be ruined. The shiver of excitement was mingled with a shudder of apprehension.

It was 6:20 A.M. In two or three more minutes, Kittinger would be on his way. I would have to kick my reservations aside now. Soon there would be much to do. I jumped to the running board of the radio truck and grabbed a microphone.

"We're almost ready, Joe. Everything okay inside?"

"No sweat," Kittinger shot back.

"Better have your cameras stowed tightly, Joe. You may get jerked a little when the balloon pulls you off."

"Roger, Major."

I looked toward the capsule. Lithe, athletic Otto Winzen was taking a last look at the suspension lines. Vera, a trim blonde in sweater and slacks, was aiming a camera to record the flight when the balloon lifted away.

At the mechanical launching arm which anchored the straining balloon, Winzen's crew stood ready for the signal to release.

Stapp moved up on the radio truck beside me.

"Everything okay?"

"He's fine," I said.

The colonel signaled to Otto Winzen with the familiar thumb-and-forefinger circle and three fingers raised.

Otto dropped an arm toward the men at the launching arm.

And the straining helium-filled balloon lifted, tugging the suspension lines sharply as it took hold of the gondola and pulled it away.

The radio crackled.

"Good-by, cruel world," Joe wisecracked.

He was off toward the heavens on man's first ascent to the atmosphere's edge.

There had been many earlier manned balloon flights, but none so ambitious as this one. Perhaps the most daring was in 1935 when Army Captains Albert Stevens and Orvil Anderson ascended to a record altitude of 72,000 feet in a 12,000-pound rubberized balloon system carried by 3,700,000 cubic feet of violently explosive hydrogen. Their record stood until November of 1956, just a few months before Kittinger's smooth take-off, when Navy Lieutenant Commanders Mal Ross and Lee Lewis flew the ball-shaped

Stratolab research gondola to 76,000 feet before crash-landing in the rolling low hills of South Dakota. But compared to Man High, the previous high-altitude gondolas had been spacious as six-room houses. Both Stevens and Anderson's *Explorer II* and the Navy *Stratolab* were large enough to walk around in. *Man High I,* in which Kittinger was ascending, was almost as cramped as a suit of armor. But it would fly at least four miles higher than Ross and Lewis had been.

For five minutes Stapp and I stood with Winzen beside the radio truck, straining our necks backward as we looked up at the rising balloon. It was climbing at a speed of about 400 feet per minute through the calm surface air, rising almost directly above us. At about 30,000 feet it would hit a 90-mile-an-hour jet stream and race speedily eastward until it rose to 35,000 feet where the winds would change sharply and the bitter-cold stratospheric temperature would plunge nearly 100 degrees below zero.

This was one of the most dangerous levels through which the balloon had to pass. Often the winds at the junction of the troposphere and stratosphere sheer off in sharp layers, like speeding cars running northward under an overpass and westward across it. If the polyethylene balloon, frozen to brittleness by the tropospheric cold, passed suddenly from a fast westward wind into an equally fast opposing wind, it would splinter like a broken light bulb. The Weather Bureau had checked these sheer winds earlier in the morning with small weather balloons and they appeared mild enough to be safe. But we could not be certain until the balloon passed through.

I made one final check of the radio system at the truck. "How is your rate of ascent, Joe?" I called.

"Up to about 500 feet a minute now," Joe replied. "No sweat so far. Everything's perfect."

I motioned to Stapp and we trotted to the waiting Sikorsky H-21 helicopter. Sergeant Dittmer, clasping the emergency medical bag beside him, was already strapped in and the chopper's air-cooled engine was idling as the pilot from nearby Wold-Chamberlain Air Force Base waited.

Now Kittinger was beginning to edge into the jet stream and the balloon was moving briskly to the east, toward Lake Michigan.

Winzen, jumping into the other helicopter, already had left for his plant to monitor the flight by the command radio system there. Stapp and I decided to stick as close as we could to the path of the balloon, hopping along near the ground below it. If by some wild chance Kittinger did attempt to bail out, I knew he would need all the medical help he could get, and quickly.

In fifteen minutes we were directly under the still rising balloon once again. I motioned to the pilot to drop into a pasture and we landed. Scrambling into the front seat of the helicopter, I picked up a microphone and pressed the switch.

"Thirty-eight, this is Thirty-five, how do you read me? Over."

He did not respond to his call sign. I waited and called again.

"How do you read me? Over."

The radio crackled.

"Thirty-five, this is Thirty-one." It was Vern Baumgartner, Otto's chief electronics engineer manning the main radio back at the plant. "We've been trying to raise him for two or three minutes now and get no response."

"Have you checked the emergency frequency?" I asked.

"Checking it now," Vern replied. "It sounds like he might be trying to send Morse code, but it's pretty garbled."

I switched the helicopter receiver to the high-frequency channel which we had set aside for emergency code use if the voice radio failed. A halting, stammering code signal was beeping through the receiver.

". . . dah-dit . . . dah-dah-dah- . . . . . . dit-dit-dit- . . . di-dah-dah . . . dit . . . di-dah . . . dah"

Joe's Morse code, learned years before when he was an aviation cadet, had obviously never been used. It was hard to make out, but I caught it as he falteringly tapped it out. The message: "N-O S-W-E-A-T."

I was grateful for my experience as a ham operator. In tuning for other hams around the world, I had become accustomed to listening to hard-to-read code signals, although most hams are quite deft at sending. And I was thankful that Joe remembered his code as well as he did, even though it was slow and halting. Most pilots, like high-school algebra students, forget their lessons completely as soon as they have passed the flight-school code test.

Stapp cupped an ear to a headset to listen to the chest microphone's signal on the low-frequency channel. It was coming through steadily and strong: "beep-a-beep, r-a-a-s-p, beep-a-beep, r-a-a-s-p." Heartbeat and respiration were only slightly above normal, indicating that although Joe probably was mildly excited by the radio emergency he was having no physical problems.

Minutes passed as he continued the slow code signals. He could hear us calling him on the VHF channel, it developed, but something prevented him from transmitting by voice.

"A-L-L-S W-E-L-L N-O S-W-E-A-T," he concluded.

We hopped over the Minnesota wheat fields below him, landing every few minutes to check again by radio. An hour and a half passed. Joe's rate of ascent had slowed to only a few feet per minute now as the balloon passed 90,000 feet. It was clear that it would ascend only a little higher. Kittinger was near peak altitude, tantalizingly under the magic mark of 100,000 feet, but still four miles higher than any other balloonist had ever been. The only man on earth who had been higher was Air Force Captain Iven Kincheloe, who arched for a few brief seconds to 126,000 feet in the Bell X-2 rocket research plane the year before. In just a few minutes at 96,000 feet, Kittinger had spent more time above virtually all of the earth's atmosphere than any man before him. I cursed the broken radio which was depriving us of his description of the dark sky of space and the earth far below. Now we would have to wait until flight's end when his impressions would not be so vivid.

"Joe, give us your checkoff list now," I called.

We had arranged before the flight for Kittinger to run down a list of items that had to be checked hourly when he was at peak altitude. To save time, each one was keyed to a number. The most important item, capsule pressure, was number 1, oxygen percentage in the atmosphere was number 2, altitude was number 3, and so forth down to oxygen quantity remaining in the main supply tank, which was number 7.

Steadily, Joe began ticking off the items, one by one, slowly tapping out the meter readings. Everything was functioning perfectly. All meters read as they should. For ten minutes he worked laboriously sending the coded signals. Then he came to oxygen quantity, one of the last items.

"I-T-E-M   S-E-V-E-N . . . . . ." Kittinger's code

84

stopped as if he was pausing to recheck his reading. It started again.

"I-T-E-M S-E-V-E-N . . . H-A-L-F."

As I scribbled his message on paper I couldn't believe my eyes.

"Joe, are you sure about Item Seven?" Archibald called back from the plant. "That's oxygen quantity in your tank and it should be almost full, not half empty."

Back came Kittinger's signal.

"D-O-U-B-L-E C-H-E-C-K-E-D . . . H-A-L-F F-U-L-L . . . W-H-A-T G-I-V-E-S"

Urgently I tried to call the Winzen plant, but the effort was fruitless. Our helicopter had moved too far away from the command radio to communicate with it clearly.

"Get me to a telephone," I shouted at the helicopter pilot. "I have to call the command center right away."

This trouble with the oxygen supply was completely unforeseen. And it was deadly serious. The gondola was equipped with a large pressurized bottle of frigid liquid oxygen, enough to last Kittinger for more than forty-eight hours if necessary. But in less than two hours half of it was gone. If a leak had sprung in the system, it might all be gone in less than an hour. Even more grave was the possibility that a leak had developed in the capsule itself. Kittinger might be in real peril of decompression miles above the earth.

Vibrating as its blades chopped through the air, the helicopter veered sharply and descended on a side road near a country filling station. The proprietor looked dumbstruck as I raced into the store in a sweat-soaked flight suit and demanded his telephone. Quickly I got Otto on the line.

"Did you see Joe's oxygen quantity report?" I asked.

"Yes," Otto replied worriedly. "Arch just questioned him again and it's less than half full."

"My God. Do you have any idea what's wrong?"

"No," said Otto. "It's definitely not a leak in the capsule itself because his capsule pressure hasn't changed at all. It might be only a faulty gauge, but we can't take a chance. If he's really lost half his oxygen in two hours he doesn't have much time left."

"Colonel Stapp and I are coming back, Otto. Meanwhile you figure out how much longer Joe can stay up with the oxygen he has left. I'll call you when we land."

I hung up and jumped back into the helicopter. In twenty minutes we were landing at Wold-Chamberlain Field. It was almost noon. The crew of the Holloman C-47 also had landed. They were prepared to take off again instantly to catch up with the balloon if it started to fall. I ran to a flight shack and called the plant.

Archibald answered the phone.

"He's lost most of the oxygen supply, Major," Arch reported. "The tank is only a tenth full now. That'll hold him for about three hours if it doesn't drain any more."

"Won't it keep on draining?"

"I don't think so," Arch replied. "We told him to turn off the oxygen converter at its supply point. That stopped whatever it is that's draining the stuff away. He can still pump oxygen in manually as he needs it."

Now there was no time to spare. If Kittinger did not begin to valve gas from the balloon and start the three-hour descent immediately, he would have to come down by parachute. There was not enough oxygen remaining to keep him alive any longer than it would take him to descend.

I wondered how Joe was reacting to the emergency. Stapp listened briefly to the heartbeat and respiration still

86

rasping and thumping over the low frequency channel. Both were still normal. The incredibly cool Captain Kittinger was even less excited than we were.

Stapp got on the radio.

"Joe, you'll have to begin your descent immediately. You have just enough oxygen left to get down, with none to spare."

We waited impatiently for Kittinger's Morse code report that he had begun valving gas.

As falteringly as a peg-legged man running uphill, the coded signal came.

"C-O-M-E A-N-D G-E-T M-E"

I was thunderstruck at his response.

Either Kittinger was joking or there was something terribly wrong. Surely he knew how grave the situation had become. If he didn't start down immediately he might not make it at all. Could Joe honestly be trying to remain aloft until he had to come down by parachute?

There was another, even worse, possibility. The weird and little understood breakaway phenomenon could be taking hold of Kittinger's mind. For some years high-altitude jet pilots had been reporting a strange sort of reverie that often overtook them when flying at extreme altitudes, a unique feeling of isolation and detachment from the earth. Many of them found the experience delightful, a sense of complete freedom from the fetters of the earth and from earthbound responsibility. But it contained the seeds of danger. After their record flight, Mal Ross and Lee Lewis reported an even more distinct "break-off" from the earth than the jet pilots described.

Following his first high altitude flight Ross described the breakaway as "a sense of complete detachment from the earth . . . a quite distinct feeling of exultation, of wanting to fly on and on." Then after the record-setting flight in November he again described the experience: "Radio voices of colleagues who were tracking in aircraft and ground vehicles were real, but they, too, seemed far away and remote. It was a sense of being physically—and almost spiritually—completely detached from earth. It was not fear nor depression, probably it was more akin to exhilaration . . . of wanting to fly on."

Kittinger's wildly improbable response to the suggestion that he come down could be an indication that he just didn't give a damn about returning to earth, that he was gripped in this strange reverie and was hell-bent on flying on and on without regard for the consequences. Like the deadly raptures of the deep, a physical reaction to great pressure that plagues divers, this strange psychological reaction to breaking away from earth may one day become known as the dangerous rapture of space.

Stapp spoke into the microphone again.

"Captain Kittinger," he called. "I assume you are only joking. If not, I am ordering you to valve as instructed. Right now."

Anxiously we awaited another report. It came.

"V-A-L-V-I-N-G G-A-S," he signaled. We had become extraordinarily exercised over a glib joke, one that is much more amusing in retrospect than it was at the time.

With relief, we turned to coffee and doughnuts. It had been eighteen hours since any of us had eaten.

Piloting one of these huge polyethylene balloons is considered by anyone who has done it every bit as difficult as flying an airplane. In one respect it is much more difficult, because it sometimes takes hours for the balloon to react to a given control.

In descending, Kittinger had to release a carefully measured amount of helium from the gas bag, just enough so that the gondola and its equipment would weigh slightly more than the lifting power of the remaining helium. To complicate the landing, the helium has more lifting ability at peak altitude than it does when it is compressed by the heavier air near the earth. So a descent begun at 400 feet per minute at 96,000 feet will double as the balloon passes through the tropopause, increasing to about 800 feet per minute. For this reason Kittinger had to be extremely careful when he began valving gas, for he was committing himself at that point to the speed with which he would hit the ground three hours later.

The trick was to begin a slow descent that would rise to about 800 feet per minute as the balloon approached the earth, then just a few hundred feet above the ground to drop ballast, lightening the load and sharply slowing the landing speed. But if too much ballast is dropped at this point, the balloon will start rising again before it ever reaches the ground and the entire landing procedure must be repeated.

In spurts Joe tapped out messages to keep us posted on his progress. It was agonizingly slow. The first valving had no detectable effect on the balloon.

Again Joe tripped the switch that opened a two-foot, electronically controlled valve at the apex of the balloon. This time he released twice the amount of gas calculated to start him downwards. Still the balloon barely moved.

Tripping the switch sporadically, hesitant lest he valve off too much gas and commit himself to a crash landing, Joe coaxed the balloon into a slow descent. Then gradually it speeded, edging toward the tropopause and back into the questionable jet stream.

As we looked up to sight the glistening balloon on its way

down all of us dismayingly noticed a high cirrus cloud overcast slipping between Kittinger and the ground. We were
losing sight of him and now we had only a radio compass to
tell us where he was.

The radio compass, unlike radar, does not give a precise
fixed location. It simply "homes" on a transmitting radio, in
this case Joe's low-frequency heartbeat channel, and points
a needle in the general direction from which the signal
comes. We knew we would have to move fast now so that
we could be in the area when he broke through the clouds.

Quickly the C-47 crew clambered back into the tracking
plane and took off to crisscross the sky, hopefully watching
for the dropping balloon. Stapp and I returned to our helicopter and lifted away once again, chopping southeast-
ward at 60 miles an hour in hopes that we would reach the
landing area before the balloon struck. Above us the C-47
was weaving a wide pattern to and fro, carefully avoiding
the cloud layer for fear of colliding with the capsule if it
suddenly broke through. And above the airplane, somewhere on top of the cloud layer, was Kittinger.

I looked up through the whirling blades of the helicopter
to see the C-47 against the clouds. Then just to the right of
it, barely discernible, I saw a faint teardrop shape at the
edge of the cloud bank.

It was Kittinger's balloon, descending 80 miles southeast
of its take-off point. It was 15 miles from us.

The helicopter banked slightly and turned to follow the
path of the balloon, now visible to the pilot. As Kittinger
reached our 400-foot altitude, directly ahead of us, we saw
three boxlike objects fall away and jerk swayingly under
recovery parachutes. He had ballasted to reduce his impact
speed.

Below us I could see a rolling meadow bounded by an

elbow-bent stream. Kittinger was drifting toward the meadow at a steady, sliding pace.

As close as the pilot dared, we followed in behind him just a few feet above the meadow. He struck near the crook-shaped creek. As the capsule hit, an electronic switch cut the balloon free and it rose again into the air, drifting away on a light ground wind.

The gondola, now free of its sustaining balloon, toppled backwards into the creek.

Urgently, Stapp and I leaped from our helicopter and ran to the quiet stream. There was no sound from the gleaming capsule save the whispering ripple of water washing around it. One window was open.

As Stapp paused to remove his shoes and roll up his trousers, I waded into the stream and peered into the open window. Kittinger's head was turned away from me, resting against the side of the gondola.

"Are you okay?" I called.

There was no answer.

Louder, I called again:

"Joe. Can you hear me?"

The still figure moved, its massive white crash helmet turning slowly.

And Kittinger's broad grin told me all was well.

I sighed with intense relief. None of my fears had materialized. Kittinger was not hurt. The capsule was undamaged except for a few minor kinks in the undercarriage. It looked solid enough to fly again immediately, except for two things: the oxygen system which had gone completely wrong, and the radio, which had hardly worked at all.

Joe waited, calmly smiling as we heaved against the capsule to set it upright at the edge of the stream. Then he climbed out. His face was flushed, his pressure suit stained dark with perspiration. Opening the suit, Colonel Stapp checked his heart.

"Still there?" Joe asked.

Stapp laughed. "It's still there."

An hour later we thumped, peered, and prodded Joe through a complete physical examination. He showed no ill effects whatever.

Without waiting any longer, Stapp, Gildenberg, Don Foster, Baumgartner, and I sat down with him in the examining room at the Wold-Chamberlain base dispensary. We wanted to know what happened.

"I don't know if anyone else saw it," said Joe, "but the balloon almost turned upside down going into the jet stream. When it edged into that wind, the balloon went clear over on its side, then as it straightened up, the capsule jerked so hard I thought it was going to snap off."

"Let's come back to that," I said. "What happened to the oxygen? You had us worried."

"I worried, too, believe me. But I haven't the foggiest notion what happened. The capsule pressure remained steady throughout the flight. So far as I could tell there was no leak. And I wasn't getting too much oxygen in the gondola. So wherever the stuff was going, it wasn't coming inside."

"How about the radio?"

"My channel-selector switch wouldn't work. After my last voice transmission, I turned it to check the other channels. It turned to the low-frequency channel okay, then popped loose, and I couldn't switch it back."

"Did you get a chance to make any outside observation?"

"Yes, but I couldn't look around very much. I was too busy with that damned code key.

"When I got to ceiling—what was it, 96,000 feet?—I could

see Lake Michigan, but not very well. About the only way I made it out was by its shape in the clouds. Most of the earth I could see was covered with a light cloud layer, but along the eastern horizon there were no clouds, and the cloudless area was shaped like Lake Michigan, so I guess that's what it was.

"I saw the moon clear as a bell, a quarter moon shining just like it does on any clear night. Brighter, but otherwise no different. I tried real hard to see if I could see the part of the moon that was in shadow. But it was just as if it wasn't there, as if there was nothing but the crescent up there.

"It was a lot easier to look up than to look down. The clouds below were so bright that they hurt my eyes."

"How about the sky color?"

"It's real strange. There's a very gradual transition from brightness right along the horizon, close to the earth, to the darkness above. It doesn't fall off in a sharp line or anything like that. It just gradually changes from almost white to light blue, then darker and darker and finally a very dark blue, almost black. It's hard to describe the color, whether it was black or blue-black. It was so dark that it was almost as if there was no color at all."

Joe was too exhausted to go on much longer. So we left him to rest.

Back at Winzen's plant, Don Foster and his crew checked the oxygen system of the capsule, which had been trucked in from the stream in which it landed. It took them only a few minutes to find the trouble.

Someone had mistakenly reversed two tubes in the oxygen system while connecting it before the flight. So instead of feeding life-giving oxygen into the capsule as it should have, the system was pumping most of it overboard. The supply tank was completely empty when Joe landed. All that was left, if Joe had remained aloft any longer, was the emergency supply in his pressure suit.

The fault with the radio was far simpler, but equally unnecessary. A tiny screw on the channel selector button had come loose. Had he recognized the problem, Joe could have fixed the loose knob with a penknife.

Despite the careful preparations and a detailed engineering check of what we thought included every item in the capsule, these two flaws had slipped by.

For want of a tightened screw and a reversed connection, we had almost lost Man High.

After his flight Kittinger was awarded the Distinguished Flying Cross and went on to another, equally hazardous research program. His new job: high-altitude parachute research. And he finally got the chance to prove that a man can survive a high-altitude jump if he is properly protected. Twice in late 1959 Joe leaped successfully from open balloon gondolas above 70,000 feet, performances demanding fantastic endurance and courage.

Chapter IV

There are times in the life of every man when the will to go on with a task, regardless of its importance, drains almost completely, like the sap of a tree that has been mercilessly hacked by a capricious woodman. In mid-June, 1957, Man High was the dying tree, its trunk virtually severed by the painful hurt of a budget cut.

The national debt was bumping against its legal ceiling and government agencies had to watch every penny they spent until Congress raised the debt limit or new tax revenues fattened the treasury. The Air Force had put the burden of economy on research. The results were disastrous. In military research centers across the country, and in countless university laboratories supported by military contracts, scientists folded up their equipment, threw out batches of experimental cultures they had worked months and even years to cultivate, and waited impatiently for new funds. Although few realized it at the time, the Russians were not so desultory. They were rushing to complete the final details of an earth satellite called *Sputnik I* that would shock the scientific pants off America. And all of the experiments that we poured into the laboratory sink during this research moratorium would take months of

95

time and millions of dollars to get started again. Some of them were lost forever.

I was in Winzen's office, sitting disconsolately on a low, modern sofa opposite the balloon manufacturer's desk. His pet boxer and constant companion, Brandy, nudged my hand, earnestly imploring me to scratch his ears. The dog, rarely out of his master's sight, usually slept under the office desk during working hours.

Stapp had phoned us from Holloman that morning to announce the Air Force order. He was hastily trying to pull all of the research programs at the Aeromedical Field Lab together to see what he could save. Some of the research, the most urgent, could continue with money on hand. But June is the end of the government's fiscal year, and few projects had funds left over to go on.

I knew that the Man High budget was near the end of its string after Kittinger's flight. We were very nearly broke and the Air Force order look like a death sentence for our program.

Kittinger's test hop, short and frantic as it was, had cut away a huge piece of our budget, but even so, it was worth every penny it cost if for no other reason than it gave us a valuable warning. The capsule obviously was not ready for a full-scale flight. To have attempted one without Kittinger's daring test could have been utterly disastrous.

With the lesson of Joe's flight before us, Colonel Stapp decided that before I could fly the balloon, the capsule would have to be checked out in a full 24-hour run under realistically simulated conditions. As soon as the Winzen company could get the capsule ready we planned to ship it to Wright Field and put it in a pressure chamber. There I would sit, breathing the same space atmosphere Kittinger used as pumps sucked the air from the chamber. I would remain at a simulated altitude of 85,000 feet for 24 hours. If there were any more bugs in the system, surely we would find them in this dress rehearsal.

But now it looked as if we would never get even that far. We were washed out completely by the Air Force order.

"Dave," Winzen said. "The company accountant has gone over cost estimates for the chamber test and your flight. The project is $14,000 short."

I had counted on getting more funds from ARDC when the new fiscal year began in July. But now the prospects were hopeless. Barring a dramatic and equally improbable change in either the national debt or in the Administration's attitude toward research, it would be at least six months, probably longer, before we could hopefully ask for money again. By then, in the bitter cold of a northern winter with its unpredictable weather patterns and high-altitude winds we probably would be stalled again, just as our first animal test of the capsule had been the previous fall.

"We could scratch the whole program," I said, rising discouraged from the sofa as Brandy scurried out of my way. "Maybe we can get Man High started again next year after this economy wave lets up."

"Do you have any idea what that would cost?" Winzen asked. "To lay everything aside, then stop what we are doing next year and start this all over again? It would double the cost. You've got to keep going now."

With dogged, Teutonic determination, he refused to acknowledge the futility of going on.

"I know how determined you are," I told him sharply. "This program has been through some awfully discouraging crises before. And you think that no matter how formidable an obstacle seems, you can get over it. Well, so do I with most of them. But this one isn't a technical problem that we can think our way out of. It's money, pure and simple. We don't have enough. And we can't get any more."

I turned and left the office. Then I walked back to the gondola room to look at the capsule that had brushed the earth's ceiling once. Two technicians were straightening the undercarriage that had bent with the impact of Joe's landing. When they finished, it sat straight on its wooden platform. But I doubted that it would ever fly again.

"She looks good as new," said one of the men.

"Yeah," the other replied. "She's been pretty successful so far."

Successful? I longed to say that word. But in scientific research, the only success is results. It doesn't matter whether the results are positive or negative. But there must be results. Bitterly, I compared myself to a chemist setting up a lab experiment. I would first prepare all of my apparatus and connect it exactly as it should be. Perhaps I would test it once to make certain I had overlooked nothing. That's what we have done here, I thought. Prepared our apparatus and tested it. But I could hardly call the experiment a success. Because there had been no experiment. This capsule was worth no more to success than a pile of unused equipment on a laboratory bench.

The next day I was gathering my papers, getting ready to return to Holloman. Any further effort here at the Winzen plant would be futile. The company simply would have to store the capsule and I would have to live on hope that we could renew the program the following year. As I stuffed papers into my briefcase, Vera Winzen, the company's vice president and production chief, called me from Otto's office.

"Can you come in here for a minute?"

Through the glass wall I could see Winzen and the company accountant, Dick Revord, poised expectantly, looking at me. Vera held the door open as I walked in. She smiled. Revord broke into a wide grin. And Otto looked thoughtfully through the glass wall of his office toward the rows of desks at which a half-dozen employees of Winzen Research Incorporated were pouring over the details of running a successful plastic bag factory.

"Dave," he said. "The company directors met last night and went over the cost figures. Dick estimates that it will cost $14,000 more than the Air Force has budgeted to complete the chamber test and get your flight off."

"So?" I asked.

"If the Air Force will agree, the company has decided to absorb the extra cost," he said softly. "The directors decided it is worth the good will and recognition a successful flight will bring to the company, and we are all betting it will be successful."

I was stunned.

Quickly I telephoned Colonel Stapp.

"It's a little unusual to have a company pay part of the cost of a government program," he said, "but I'm sure we can get it cleared."

I was as happy as a five-year-old on Christmas Day. Now we could go ahead. We could fly *Man High II* into the upper atmosphere in August, only two months away.

The chamber run had to be as nearly realistic as possible, because it was the final rehearsal. If we overlooked anything there, the flight could easily fail. We had seen how immense two small mistakes could become on Joe's ascent. On the full-scale flight, we could not afford even one minor error. It had to be perfect.

Three days before the scheduled test, I checked into the

bachelor officers' quarters at Wright Air Development Center. The capsule arrived by air on the same day and had been set up beside an ungainly pressure chamber at Wright Field's Instrumentation Test Section. The chamber looked like a huge pressure cooker with windows. Its dome-shaped top lifted off and an overhead crane stood ready to raise the capsule and set it inside. Briefly, I watched Winzen busily supervising capsule preparations, then I turned to medical plans.

Arch and Sergeant Dittmer were preparing a set of electrodes that would signal a complete electrocardiograph trace of the pulsations of my heart during the test. The electrodes, sensitive to minute changes in the currents generated by the heart muscle as it contracts and relaxes, would instantly alert them to circulatory problems that might crop up under the stressful effects of breathing an alien atmosphere under uncomfortable, isolated and confined conditions.

I would take my own oral temperature from time to time and report that. And a tight belt around my chest would send a signal that showed my breathing rate as my chest rose and fell. Colonel Stapp would have more medical information from me than we had taken from Kittinger on his flight.

With Captain George Ruff, a Wright Aeromedical Lab psychiatrist who already had become expert in human stress experiments, I devised a chart on which to record my own observations of my mental condition during the flight. It was a crude personal assessment of my efficiency, a chart on which I would rate myself both during this test and during the real flight according to how efficiently I thought I was performing my scientific and piloting tasks. If I felt alert and eager, I would grade efficiency at 100 per cent.

If I felt my interest ebbing, or if I felt physical strain eating away at mental efficiency, I would lower the grade.

During the chamber test, Ruff planned to look in on me occasionally to see if he could detect any effects from isolation and monotony. Little research had been done on this subject, but both of us suspected that the utter loneliness of a single man isolated in space could lead to mental effects that might sap his will, distort his judgment, and possibly hurt him physically. I remembered well the curious relationship between a mental problem—claustrophobia—and physical collapse that had overcome the alternate Man High scientist after his seemingly routine claustrophobia test. Even so, the chances of isolation and particularly monotony really hurting me seemed remote. I already had so much planned to do on my flight that I expected monotony to be the least of my problems.

My diet for the three days before the test was carefully restricted to what we call low-residue foods such as gelatin, fish, and lean steak which are almost totally absorbed by the body in digestion, leaving only a small residue of waste. The reason for this was obvious. Man High was not large enough to contain a men's room, and even if it did, pressure suits are not built with a flap in the back. I had to prepare myself for restrained bathroom habits whether I liked it or not.

On the day before the test I awoke at 7 A.M. to contribute a specimen to Archibald's urinalysis program. He was studying my excretion of adrenal hormones to get an index of the physical stress to which I would be subjected. As stress increased, the hormone count also would increase. At the same time, Sergeant Knox, one of Arch's assistants, took a 20-cc. blood sample from my arm for a check of hormone blood level. Then at hourly intervals from 10 A.M.

until 2 P.M., Miss Eunice Hugoniot, a Holloman lab technician, pricked my fingers for small blood samples. Before the
real flight this would be done again to check the average
number of a kind of abnormal white blood cells called
binucleated lymphocytes in my body. Dr. Lowry Dobson,
of the University of California, suspected that cosmic radiation might significantly increase the number of these
abnormal cells. And although there would be no cosmic
radiation in the pressure-chamber test, Miss Hugoniot went
ahead with her sampling to establish a normal average for
later comparison. The next morning I gave blood and urine
again, then went to the pressure chamber. I would enter
the capsule at 9 A.M.

As I dressed for the test, Archibald and Sergeant Dittmer
carefully taped their instruments to my body and the
pressure suit was zipped shut. I stepped into the capsule
carrying six candy bars and three sandwiches, my snacks
for the next twenty-four hours. Then one by one, Arch
handed in and checked off the things I would need inside
the capsule: Chest parachute, tape recorder, cameras, just
as if this was a real flight.

Before the test had even begun there was trouble. I sat
patiently inside, wincing as wrenches clanked against the
sides of the capsule while engineers wrestled with an air-
conditioner connection that would not fit. In three hours it
was repaired, but by then another problem was ready to
take its place. The capsule still had not been pressurized,
yet it was leaking oxygen. More hours drained from the
schedule as Archibald and Don Foster looked for the
trouble. They found it in an emergency valve. But by then
so much oxygen had escaped that the whole test had to be
delayed while a new valve was installed and the oxygen
tank refilled.

It was well that we had decided on the chamber test before the flight. If this valve failure had gone undetected until my ascent, I would hardly have been able to reach the stratosphere, much less remain there for a day. Wearily I climbed out of the capsule. I had been inside for six hours.

For four hours I cat-napped in the blessed coolness outside the capsule. Then I climbed back in and Archibald flushed my atmosphere to the 60 per cent oxygen, 20 per cent nitrogen, and 20 per cent helium I would breathe for the next day. Gently, a crane assembled my capsule in the potlike chamber and its lid was sealed. But even now I had to wait another six hours before the chamber could be depressurized, putting me at a simulated altitude of 85,000 feet. Before the pressure could be lowered in the chamber, its walls had to be thoroughly soaked with bitterly freezing 70-degree-below-zero air. We wanted to duplicate the temperature of the upper atmosphere. Before the chamber's heavy-duty pumps sucked away the air around the capsule, I was sitting inside a box that was twice as cold as a food freezer. For a time inside my space cabin, I was comfortably warmed by my own body heat circulated over and over again by the air-regeneration system. But soon it became uncomfortably cold. Later, the chamber operators lighted infra-red lamps to simulate the intense heat of the daytime sun, and the water-can cooler mounted on the undercarriage outside exuded a faint mist that carried my body heat and the heat of the electrical circuits in the gondola away.

Seriously, I concentrated on the jobs I would have to do when I did go aloft. First I picked up my spot photometer, a light-measuring device that looks more like the telescopic sight on an elephant gun than the delicate optical apparatus that it is. Its lens focuses on a single spot in the sky, excluding the diffused light from the earth, the sun, and other sources, and with a complicated photoelectric cell measures the brightness of the spot at which it is aimed. Without it any measurement of sky brightness would be as inaccurate as that of an ill-equipped photographer who tries to get an exact light reading by guessing at the reflectivity of his subject. Unless he is lucky, his color pictures will always be bad. Any purely visual judgments I made would be equally bad and generalized in fuzzy, scientifically worthless terms like "hazy" or "very bright." The spot photometer, literally only an extremely complex and specialized photographic light meter, would give me exact measurements of brightness for particular spots in the sky. With these measurements, researchers at the Air Force's Cambridge Research Laboratory at Massachusetts Institute of Technology, could duplicate exact upper atmosphere and space-light situations to tell them what kind of targets a person could see at very high altitudes and at what angles the targets might disappear from sight. The experiment had been planned, and the instrument provided, by Dr. S. Q. Duntley of the Scripps Institution of Oceanography, whose interest was in calculating from the light intensity of the atmosphere how much dust, water vapor, and other foreign material was scattered at very high altitudes.

Soberly practicing with the gunlike meter, I carefully read the bright reflectivity of the pressure chamber's painted steel walls. One by one, I checked the other pieces of practical and scientific paraphernalia aboard.

The five-inch telescope returned a bright but out-of-focus image when I aimed it toward the walls of the chamber. But its motor-driven mirror, with which I could scan a 180-degree arc of the sky, operated perfectly. As I pressed switches near the eyepiece inside the gondola, two tiny motors slowly moved the mirror on the outside through an arc that would pick up 50 per cent of the visible sky when I flew. I was wildly excited about the possibilities the telescope offered. Although simple and small enough to fit inside the viewing stool of the giant 200-inch Hale telescope at Mount Palomar Observatory, it would see the nearby planets and stars and galaxies as the Hale had never seen them, for it would be above the distracting shimmering of the earth's atmosphere whose layers of air, varying widely in temperature and loaded with water vapor, severely distort any image reaching an earth-bound astronomer. Although fascinated by astronomy since childhood, I knew that I was too ill-trained to make more than one genuinely useful contribution to the science. I could prove that viewing from a balloon-borne observatory is practical. Later, when high-altitude balloon flights became routine, astronomers could go aloft for more meaningful observations. By using diffraction gratings in special telescopes, they could read with precision such things as the chemical geography of other planets. Water vapor and oxygen, for instance, absorb certain wave lengths of light at the infra-red end of the spectrum. By spreading the light of Mars on a spectrograph with a diffraction grating, then studying the result to see which bands of light were missing due to absorption by the red planet's atmosphere, they could tell precisely how much water vapor or oxygen or other constituents the Martian atmosphere contains. From the earth this can not be done accurately because our own atmospheric water vapor and oxygen stand between the spectrographic telescopes and Mars. The information could tell us much about the nature of life on our neighbor planet.

Studying Venus by the same method, astronomers could

for the first time penetrate the mystery that lies beneath the thick veil of carbon dioxide which shrouds the sister planet of earth so completely that her surface never has been seen.

Eventually, with a large enough reflecting mirror, they could see the "planet" Pluto clearly and perhaps settle the long-standing controversy over whether it is really a planet or simply a "lost moon" of Neptune, flung into a solar orbit eons ago. Many of the mysteries of the cosmos would be clarified if the astronomers could get "good seeing," as they call it, from a platform above the atmosphere.

Feeling foolish over the waste of film, I trained my 16-millimeter Cinekodak out a porthole near my head and ground away at the out-of-focus images of Archibald, Stapp, and the others as they peered through the multi-layered glass portholes of the chamber. I had never used the camera before, and needed the practice now so I would not have to waste time with puzzling photographic problems during the flight. I also shot the same dull scene with my own Nikon 35-millimeter still camera. The pictures I took on the real flight could be of great scientific value whether they were esthetically interesting or not. On a broader scale, they would perform the same function as the spot photometer. With accurate color pictures of the earth's horizon, I could give future space pilots a view of the earth and its atmosphere as they will see it when they re-enter after orbital or deep space flight. I could also photograph precisely the changing light pattern of the sky as the sun rose and set.

During the night I concentrated on the capsule itself, carefully checking its atmospheric system, guarding against an excessive build-up of deadly carbon dioxide, watching my own physical symptoms, and recording my own judgment of my ability to perform on the efficiency chart. Sporadically, I napped. With so much to occupy mind and time, the dress rehearsal seemed far less tiring than my first claustrophobia test. There was no longer any question that the business of the actual flight would be so diverting in itself that I would have no time for concern over the discomforts of the capsule.

But a less esoteric feeling was now taking hold of me. My abdomen was grabbing tightly in diarrhea cramps, churning periodically with the distracting pain and urgency of that familiar disorder.

Later in the morning my bladder seemed filled to what felt like the floating point, yet I could do nothing about it. Although provision had been made for the latter function in the gondola as a part of Arch's physiological test, I was distractingly unable to separate the two ordinary processes. Like a man with a gold nugget and a hot penny in his hand, I couldn't let go of one without dropping the other.

By mid-afternoon I would cheerfully have given all the wealth in the world for the brief use of a common household fixture. So at 4 P.M. we stopped the test. I doubt that any pilot before or since has slipped out a tight-fitting pressure suit as fast.

Aside from my personal problem, the test had proven the capsule airworthy. It would have to be carefully pressure-checked before the flight to guarantee against a repetition of the oxygen valve leak, but otherwise it was in perfect shape. The air-regeneration equipment, a pressure-sealed container holding three absorbent chemicals through which the capsule air was constantly driven, had performed beautifully. It was like a triple sink. In one section, anhydrous lithium chloride absorbed excess water. In another, anhydrous lithium hydroxide absorbed deadly car-

bon dioxide, and in the third, anhydrous magnesium
perchlorate took up additional water which the first sink
missed. A centrifugal blower shoved 25 cubic feet of the
capsule air through the spongelike unit every minute. The
system was not designed to work on a long flight in space
because in time the chemicals would become saturated
with CO_2 and water. But the chamber test and past flights
with animals had proved that it would hold up long
enough for my 24-hour flight, with a margin of safety of a
few hours.

I emerged from the test as airworthy as the capsule itself,
in spite of my hurry to get out. Arch and Sergeant Dittmer,
backed up by two Wright Field physiologists, found nothing alarming in my electrocardiograph or respiration, although they were frustrated during the test when some of
the sensors they had strapped to my body stopped working.
And psychologically I felt fit as a fiddle. My efficiency chart
was consistently marked above 90 per cent.

We did not learn until much later how naïve we were to
accept this judgment at its face value. No man's mind is
strong enough to assess itself realistically when severely
stressed and fatigued. As the mind's efficiency slips, so does
its judgment.

Back in Minneapolis, we began to make our final preparations. The flight already was becoming a major inter-
service event. Such Army-Navy-Air Force co-operation
usually escapes attention, but it has become a healthy and
ordinary practice in the field. While infrequent inter-
service squabbles grab headlines in Washington, officers
and men at the working level of all three services swap
ideas and help as if they all wore the same uniform.

The Office of Naval Research loaned a big radio
communications van and another truck which had been in

service at Minneapolis during the Navy's Skyhook weather balloon program. The Army, advised that we needed two helicopters to supplement the one tracking chopper the Air Force assigned to Man High, sent two craft with full crews up from a base in Georgia. And Air National Guardsmen at Wold-Chamberlain helped with the thankless task of flying the capsule back from Wright Field. There was no bickering, no jockeying for position, no striving to be foremost. There were only men who saw and understood a job that needed doing and did it.

From Washington, where he had his laboratory, Dr. Herman Yagoda flew in to lend a hand with our cosmic radiation study. Yagoda, an Air Force Cambridge Research Center scientist and one of the world's leading cosmic ray experts, brought photographic track plates which would be strapped to my arms and chest. Any cosmic particles which struck those regions during the flight would leave a trace on the film. By comparing the film to my skin, we would be able to tell precisely where the particles entered my body. Tiny tattoos would be etched on my skin at the corners of the film plates so that we would never loose track of the exact positions. I would submit myself to years of study to see what effect the space radiation might have.

Yagoda also brought a second batch of film emulsions which he wanted to send aloft with the balloon as a hitchhike experiment. These he would study after the flight to determine the nature of the cosmic particles which penetrated them.

Another scientific hitchhiker was a bundle of tubes filled with neurospora mold, sent for cosmic ray study by Dr. A. Gib DeBusk of Florida State University.

A third scientist, Dr. Daniel Johnson of the National Bureau of Standards, arrived with a carefully sealed barograph with which to record the official altitude of the flight. Normally the Air Force frowns on attempts to set "official" records because frequently they are conducted for their own sakes. But on our flight an official record attempt was approved, providing we found someone other than the Air Force to pay for it. In order to have a flight officially recorded by the Fédération Aëronautique Internationale and thereby stamped in the formal world record books, it is necessary to defray the expenses of sending a scientific observer with carefully calibrated equipment into the field. *Life* magazine, anxious to publish my story after the flight, had graciously and discretely offered the $3,500 it cost to have Dr. Johnson retained by the FAI to make the record official.

The hot July days ran by me one by one. The flight was now only a week away. More and more excited about the coming ascent, I had submerged my personal life almost completely as I concentrated on the innumerable details of Man High. And just as my fascination with the sea of details and exuberance over the growing likelihood of a perfect flight a week hence reached their peak, the floodgate that had dammed back my personal life broke.

My attachment to the Simons Clinic in Lancaster never had grown much beyond a boyhood fascination with the upstairs laboratory and Hiram Miller. And this had been a huge disappointment to my father. He had hoped during my boyhood and medical training that I would take over his busy general practice when he retired. We were never very close in those years, but I knew his hope.

As a boy I saw my father mostly as an imposing figure who was almost constantly out on house calls or working in his office across the street. A profound sense of responsibility and dedication to his profession and his patients made him thus, and I respected him all the more for it. But as I became more fascinated with electronics and with research far removed from general medicine, I could see his disappointment. It was not until he saw some of the same dedication in me that we began to grow closer. As a physician he recognized the value of the challenge we had accepted in Man High, and soon he became as excited over the problems and the determined struggle against discouraging setbacks as I was.

In January, months before we had even begun to plan the Kittinger flight, my father acknowledged a terrible new relationship to his beloved medicine. He had an inoperable cancer of the stomach. In the months that followed, whenever I could grab a few hours away from Man High, I rushed home to Lancaster to see him. Eagerly he followed the details of the Man High program. But he was sinking.

On Father's Day, just after Joe's flight, I saw him for the last time. He was fascinated with Kittinger's experience and he looked forward anxiously to my flight.

Flying back to Minneapolis from this visit, I looked down across the Allegheny Mountains and saw a pattern of life stretching far beyond my eyes: hills clearly discernible just below me, peaks shrouded in mist and too shadowy to define up ahead, and mere suggestions of further crests far beyond. It was thus that Sam Simons, M.D., retired and now dying, had viewed life: the events immediately upon him clear and distinct; the future barely distinguishable but visible and worthy of attention, and the most distant events a reality only in faith.

I was happy and thankful that Man High was approaching its climax. It was the one dimly seen peak which could capture his interest and focus it beyond the despair and pain with which he had to live.

For the next six weeks there were no hours left for the hurried but gratifying visits home. Then six days before my scheduled flight, he died. His heart had failed, many weeks, perhaps months, before the cancer would have claimed him.

Sadly, I returned to Lancaster, wondering if I should go on with Man High. And as I crossed the mountains again, I thought of the man who had never wavered from his ideals and his dedication to healing. I knew that he would follow through, to see the mist roll back from the dimly seen peak ahead and win a small but all-important glimpse of the still unseen hills beyond.

I returned to Minneapolis, determined to go on.

Friday, August 15 arrived. The weather was uncertain, but Duke Gildenberg, after methodically checking the high altitude winds as far west as the Soviet Union, saw a slight possibility that we could take off the next morning. Don Foster planned to bottle me up in the capsule at the Winzen plant, then proceed by a truck-led caravan to Crosby, 90 miles to the north, where we would use the Hanna mine pit as a natural protective bowl to shield the balloon from winds above the surface during the inflation. But I would have to be sealed up earlier than Kittinger had been in order to give extra time for the three hour trip to Crosby. I was to be shut inside the capsule at 11 P.M. the night before the scheduled early morning launch.

I wanted as much rest as I could possibly get before the time of the flight. Once sealed in the confining capsule, it was doubtful if I could snatch more than a few hours of sleep for the next two days.

Colonel Stapp gave me two seconal tablets at 11 A.M., and I dropped into my motel bed not far from the plant. Irritated, I half-awoke from the drugged sleep to allow

Eunice Hugoniot to puncture my right forefinger for a blood sample. Again at 1 P.M. and 2 P.M. she deftly pricked my fingers as I barely awakened, eyelids heavy from the seconal. The drug soon wore off and I awoke with a start at 6 P.M.

Could this be it? Was I at last to go into this strange realm about which I had dreamed for two years? Quickly I dressed and drove with Colonel Stapp to a roadside restaurant. My last low-residue meal, brought by a puzzled waitress who could not understand why I would not take the salad and desert—"but sir, they come with the meal, you'll pay for them anyway"—was lean rare steak. I longed for fresh vegetables, but remembering my cramps during the pressure-chamber test, I willingly pushed them aside.

As we arrived at the plant, the night sky was beginning to cloud over. And the look on Duke Gildenberg's face told me I had not yet eaten my last low-residue meal. The weather was closing in with possible rain squalls and gusty ground winds forecast for the next morning. My flight was canceled.

With the optimistic pleasure of a confirmed Pollyanna, I returned to the motel room for more sleep. It had been a tiring two weeks. I welcomed the chance to rest another night before starting the preflight routine again.

The next day, Saturday, I busily turned the morning to a final check of my equipment. And again at 11 A.M. I fell into a seconal-induced sleep at the motel. Once again Miss Hugoniot self-consciously slipped into the room with her infernal needle. I shook loose from the seconal long enough to mumble jokingly, "Thank you, Miss Vampira," as she stepped out after the third blood-letting.

The same waitress looked curiously on and Colonel Stapp laughed as I gulped another low-residue dinner.

And again we drove to the rambling one-story Winzen plant, more warily this time than the night before. The weather still looked questionable, but Gildenberg thought it might clear. We decided to go ahead with the preparations and make our last weather check just before I was ready to climb into the gondola.

With great care Arch and Dittmer taped the stethoscopic microphone above my heart and attached the cosmic ray film plates to my arms and chest. Then hopefully I zipped shut the suit and walked down the long, narrow corridor leading from the dressing room to the gondola room in the back of the plant.

Hanging from the walls of the corridor were a hundred framed photographs of balloons and animals and experiments conducted in the years before. It was like ambling through my own past, seeing the familiar scenes of less hazardous events before this night. I looked earnestly at some of the photographs, thirstily soaking up the familiar details. In one of the frames was a reprint of a *Time* magazine cover picture showing an artist's idealized view of Colonel Stapp as he rocketed at 640 miles an hour down the Holloman test track. I wondered how he had felt as he walked to his rocket sled.

Like me? Confident that every detail had been taken care of, that nothing had been overlooked? In many ways I thought of the flight as being less hazardous than a cross-country drive, for here we had nurtured every possible hazard in our minds and knew where the dangers lay. In a sense, we anticipated the unexpected and prepared for it. On a road trip, one cannot anticipate the erratic behavior of the "other driver."

Duke Gildenberg met me at the capsule and held up his hand as I started to climb in.

The weather was not clearing. We would have to cancel again.

With a sigh I returned to the dressing room and painfully removed the film plates and the stethoscopic mike we had taped so firmly in place. As I pulled the adhesive tape away from a hair covered chest I winced at the thought of repeating the agony again, and at the possibility of even more delay.

Wide awake after so much sleep in two days of false preparation, I hung around the plant, organizing and reviewing the experiments I had to conduct. A television film crew, awakened by Winzen's public relations man, Joe Groth, and apprised of the fact that I was relatively free to posture for their cameras, sleepily set up their equipment in front of the capsule and tried to exhaust a seemingly endless reservoir of film as I posed and pointed, explaining the mechanics of the capsule and the purpose of the flight.

But despite the night of sleeplessness I had to fall back on seconal again as I dropped into the motel bed at 11 A.M. With the regularity of a dripping faucet Miss Vampira returned on the hour to shake me out of a drugged sleep and draw more blood. My fingertips, punctured like ten vegetable colanders, were becoming quite sore. At 6 P.M. I arose sluggishly, glancing out of the motel room window to see a clouded evening sky. After all our problems, surely we aren't going to repeat the long vigil of last fall, I thought, as I methodically reached for the telephone to check with Gildenberg.

"Don't hold me in suspense, Duke. I'm tired enough to go back to bed if you're planning another cancellation."

"It looks hopeful, Dave," Duke said, his tone curiously defensive.

"Doesn't look any better than yesterday from my window," I grumpily observed, dropping the receiver into its hook.

Still stumbling sleepily, I shuffled into the bathroom and fumbled as I hooked my two electric shavers together. Several years before, determined to find extra time to add to a pressing work schedule, I discovered that using two shavers instead of one cut shaving time in half. I doubted if I needed the time tonight, but I raced through the process anyway.

Fully awake now, I carefully set aside a bottled urine sample for Archibald's physiological test. He would compare it with samples taken during the flight and a final sample after the flight to count the increased hormone excretion associated with anticipation and stress.

Colonel Stapp joined me as I was ready to leave for another monotonous dinner of lean red steak. I still longed for forbidden vegetables.

"Did you call the plant?" he asked.

"Yes. Gildenberg says it looks hopeful. He must be wearing dark glasses and reading someone else's weather map," I added, looking at the cloud-strewn sky.

"I suppose he sees a high-pressure area moving in to sweep this stuff away," Stapp said.

"It'll have to be a big one to push all of this weather out of the way," I mused.

Gildenberg met us at the plant door.

"Come here," he called, motioning to a blackboard sketch of the weather map. He pointed to two distinct pressure-front symbols. One was a clear and calm high-pressure area that was just beginning to edge into Minnesota. Behind it was a huge low-pressure front nudging the slow-moving high from the far southwest.

"This high will be in here by midnight and give us clear sailing," Duke said soberly. "It's pretty stable and should stick around the plains states for at least forty-eight hours before that low moves in," he pointed to the ominous weather symbol in the southwest. "The low will generate thunderheads and considerable electrical disturbance, so we don't want any part of it. But it's a good two days away. If you get away in the morning, you should be back on the ground for a half a day before it gets here."

I looked questioningly at Stapp and at Otto Winzen who had joined us.

"If Duke says it, it must be so," Stapp smiled.

"Same here," said Otto.

"Okay," I said. "But it looks like there's more hope than certainty on this map, Duke. I'd almost bet this overcast won't move out until noon tomorrow."

"Want to bet?" There was testy edginess in Duke's normally taciturn manner.

"No," I laughed. "Not this time. You're too lucky. Besides, with money on it, you won't give up until we're blown off the launching site."

Philosophically, I went through the arduous process of dressing and taping the stethoscope and film plates to my skin. After two postponements I was a confirmed pessimist. And I was enough of a meteorologist to suspect that Duke's forecast of "hopeful" clearing probably meant another cancellation.

Unknown to me, Duke was wrestling with his own conscience. A quiet, meticulously careful scientist by nature and by training, he was preparing to go much farther than a simple bet on his forecast. He was bending to an urge to take a tremendous gamble. And the stake in the gamble was my life.

Duke knew far more than appeared on the weather map he showed us. But he kept it to himself. There was a good chance, he knew, that a violently churning storm front in the southwest would slide very quickly over the northern plains and hang there, like a shield of lightning, to block my return to the ground once I was launched. There was an equally good chance, he knew, that it would hold back forty-eight hours or slip quickly past below me, like a wave sliding under a surfboard, bringing a brief wave of calm weather behind it for a safe landing.

Duke feared that if we waited to see how stable the calm high-pressure area expected by launch time would be, it would be too late to take advantage of it. And behind the storm front that menacingly confronted him, he knew there would be no ideal flying weather for at least three weeks. The symbols on the weather map added up to one thing in Duke's mind. Get it off now, or wait the better part of a month. If the trouble that had plagued Man High in the past was an indication, more delay now would be an open invitation to more frustrating problems as we waited for the weather to clear. He knew as well as I did that financially, if for no other reason, it was now or never. We literally could not afford delay.

Duke seemed withdrawn and even morose. But none of us knew why. He was having a soul-wrenching argument with himself, fighting down the careful instincts of a trained scientist.

Unaware of Duke's problem, I squeezed into my suit, now almost as familiar to me as the Air Force uniform I had worn for nine years, and trudged awkwardly back to the gondola room. There Foster had finished his check of the structure. I climbed in backwards, slipping onto the nylon net of the seat. Carefully I checked over the items I would need if the flight did go off, a possibility that I still doubted. My cameras were snugly clamped to the capsule wall in a case made especially for them. Two polyethylene bags and a metal rack held film. Below my chair were plastic bottles for urine samples. I shuddered at the reminder of the cramping attack during the pressure chamber dress rehearsal and looked for the emergency medical kit. It was beside me. Unzipped beneath me on the seat was a thermal suit already in place where I could zip it on if the nighttime temperature drop in the capsule became too uncomfortable. A label on the soft pile-lined coat was turned up to show its "2-Clo" classification, an arbitrary measurement that meant the suit would bestow the equivalent warmth of two full suits of clothes, from topcoat to skin.

Directly in front of my face, a chest-pack parachute dangled from a hook on the frame of the capsule. It was tightly packed, untouched since I had checked it the night before. Dr. Johnson of the Bureau of Standards swung it aside to peer in, then quickly calculated that the total volume of equipment and man inside the three-by-eight-foot capsule was roughly equivalent to that of a man with six packed suitcases inside a telephone booth. Actually, I thought, the telephone booth would be a little roomier.

I turned my head toward the right side of the domed upper hemisphere to a homemade cardboard talisman forwarded from my children. On one side they had pasted a map of the face of the moon. On the other side their fingerprints and scrawled signatures, Suzie, Sammie, Sally, and Scotty, were inscribed under a note: "When you reach this, come home."

Suddenly Otto thrust in a paper box which smelled slightly of the oils of a short-order kitchen. It was my food for the flight: two cans of Air Force flight rations, four cans of fruit juice, four sandwiches, six candy bars, and a can of nuts.

"Eat heartily," he joked, and "Good luck. We're ready to seal you in now."

My God, I thought, they really mean to go through with it this time. Gildenberg must have picked up another hopeful forecast. Or else they're just playing it to the hilt just in case the weather clears when Duke thinks it will.

Colonel Stapp, a notorious punster whose quips sometimes fall somewhat short of Shakespearean standards, reached in to shake hands.

"Major," he said, "you will soon reach the high point of your career."

In the background, Vera was snapping the scene with a Rolleiflex. At 10:40 P.M., the framework in which I sat was raised then slowly lowered into the shell of the capsule, and I was hermetically sealed, as tightly as canned meat on a grocery store shelf. Outside, Arch turned the controls that flushed my atmosphere and replaced it with the rich oxygen-nitrogen-helium mixture we had used before. I talked into the microphone, tickled at the octave-high sound of my voice. But quickly, with only a slight throat-tightening effort, it settled back to normal.

I peered out of the narrow portholes for a last look at the brightly lighted gondola room as four technicians shifted me onto a fork lift and trundled the capsule to a waiting flat-bed truck parked at the loading ramp in back. There Don Foster packed the upper dome with dry ice, and the caravan crept slowly out to the highway. The truck bumped slowly along, leading the caravan on the ninety-mile ride to Crosby. I worried about the incessant jostling fearful that it might break the essential but fragile Beckman oxygen meter. We can check it again when we get to the pit, I thought. I'd better sleep now. I dozed.

Behind the capsule truck came the Winzens and Stapp, riding inside the large communications van we had borrowed from the Navy. Inside it were four bunks. They slept, too, as the Man High space capsule bumped northward, steaming like a smouldering fire under the 50-pound cap of dry ice.

As the trucks wound down a curving road that descended along the edge of the circular mine, I awoke and stared out at what looked like a Dantean vision of hell. Fog was rolling down the jagged, rust-red walls of the 425-foot-deep pit, swirling across the roadway. Near the bottom of the mine pit, the Winzen crew already was rolling the giant plastic balloon along its protective carpet, laying the folded polyethylene out for inflation.

Now I know they mean it, I thought. They would never unfurl the balloon unless they were certain of the weather. Once unrolled, the balloon cannot be bundled up again and reused.

I switched my radio to the VHF frequency over which we would conduct all our communications.

"How's the weather look now?" I called.

"It's a good thing you didn't take Duke's bet," Vern Baumgartner, the Winzen communications chief, called back. "It's clear as a bell and ground winds are barely one-mile-an-hour."

"It doesn't pay to gamble with Gildenberg," I joked.

Now I knew it was positive. I was going at last to the edge of space to see and study what no man had carefully observed before. The muscles in my abdomen shimmered with the familiar butterflies, much as they had before my first parachute jump and as I taxied to the runway for my first solo plane flight.

Then another familiar feeling came over me. It was much like the feeling I have had when I leave the house in the morning, dimly aware that I have forgotten something but unable to remember what it is. Even a return trip to the house will not jog the feeling loose. It was born of a sense of responsibility, almost a preliminary guilt which was forcing me to review in my mind everything I must do on the flight, every observation I must make, every switch, every movement, every note to be recorded. I must miss nothing.

Later, my body tingled with the mixture of apprehension and excitement that is born of the finality of commitment to an unknown. It was a pleasant sensation, the same sort of a feeling I suppose that forces other men to demand the chance to make of themselves fools or heroes; to willingly, even eagerly embrace an event whose hazards may range from the discovery of unforeseen cowardice to death. Already I was beginning to savor the anticipation of overcoming the hazards, commanding the event; the thrill of winning infinitely enhanced for a scientist by the thrill of discovery.

I settled down to the serious work of systematically checking all of my equipment once again. All radio channels checked out; all flight controls; all personal equipment; the telescope motor; the Beckman oxygen meter which had worried me on the bumpy ride to Crosby. Everything checked out perfectly. I called Arch on the VHF and read off the itemized checkout list. There were no omissions.

The porthole windows of the gondola had fogged over from the frosty, swirling vapor of the dry ice, but Colonel Stapp called periodically to report the balloon inflation was going off without a hitch. Then his voice became worried.

"I'm afraid the wind is rising a little bit, Dave," he said. "We'll have to hurry now or we might get caught."

We were running behind schedule and the morning calm was disappearing.

Stapp and Otto had ample grounds for worry, and so did I. If the winds rose above five miles an hour at the top of the pit, they would catch the thirty-story-high balloon and whip it like a sail, dashing it and perhaps me as well against the jagged iron ore that pocked the sides of the mine.

Moments later, Otto came on. There was more trouble.

A reinforced plastic band had become stuck around the base of the balloon after inflation, gripping it tig.itly like a wound rubber band around the neck of an inflated toy balloon. It was thirty feet above ground level and no one had a ladder. To ascend with the bottom of the balloon sealed by that band would be suicidal, since heat and diminishing air pressure at altitude would cause the helium inside the balloon to expand. When the expansion reached this band, the balloon would surely burst.

"We've sent up to the mine headquarters for a ladder, Dave. Just hold on. We'll get it," Stapp called.

He sounded more worried than ever. Anxiously I tried to peer out the fogged portholes, but they were too heavily covered. I could imagine their worry. The wind was rising and we were losing precious time.

The minutes ticked by. Ten, fifteen, twenty. Each time he called me, Stapp's voice rose higher with anxiety.

Then at last the ladder arrived. And with relief in his voice, Colonel Stapp gave me a running account of the action. Vera, who confessed to a lifelong fear of going higher than the second rung of a kitchen stool, bravely climbed the ladder as six Winzen men held it, bracing to keep it from brushing the delicate plastic bag. As production chief of the Winzen company, Vera was the only person there thoroughly enough accustomed to working with the fragile stuff who could be trusted to snip away the constricting band without pricking a hole in the balloon. Carefully edging her scissors beneath it, she cut away the band.

But now the wind had risen to the danger point.

Otto, with only minutes remaining, decided to edge the balloon and capsule deeper into the mine to find more space for the launching. Slowly the capsule truck rolled down the narrow road. The balloon already was towering above me, attached to the gondola and tugging upwards. Around the base of the capsule, six of Winzen's men firmly held me down. I looked out the window and saw the scene around me clearly for the first time since we had entered the pit. Foster had removed the frost and moisture on my portholes.

Halfway down the road the truck stopped.

Time had run out. It was now or never.

"Let her go," Otto shouted.

Like a giant pendulum, the capsule swung wildly toward the canyon-steep wall of the mine pit.

Chapter V

The jagged, rust-scarred walls of the iron mine seemed to fall away from me as the capsule swung upward, twisting and arcing widely like a pendulum on a giant grandfather clock. And like a pendulum at the top of its arc the capsule paused within a yard of one of the pocked cliffs and swung away. I was too busy recording the thrilling moment on movie film to realize how close I had come to having my hopes and myself as well dashed against the unforgiving iron ore of the mine pit. The time was 9:22 A.M. This capsule now rising gently away from the earth would be my world for the next thirty-two hours. Before I left it in a South Dakota flax field I would be joyously thrilled over the things it could do for me. And I would fear, almost to the point of panic, the things it could do *to* me.

But now I stared with fascination out the porthole at my left shoulder. A split mirror mounted just outside reflected the balloon and the sky above in its top surface and the fading outline of the launching pit on its underside. Through the mirror's top side I saw the giant polyethylene balloon sparkling brightly with sunlight and fluttering in the turbulent air as it rose into the sky. The bubble of helium at its apex tugged the great gas bag upward like a huge inverted teardrop whose sides fell in rippling pleats that trailed down as gracefully as the soft folds of a girl's formal gown swirling across a ballroom.

I watched the reflection in the mirror's underside nostalgically and with curious detachment as the tiny figures in the iron mine grew smaller and smaller and disappeared. An ever broadening view of the dense Minnesota forest spread beneath me, broken in beautiful random patches by the golden reflection of sunlight on hundreds of tiny lakes that seemed to huddle protectively under a fluffy canopy of summer cumulus clouds. For a few seconds a wispy fogginess enveloped the capsule as it rose silently and swiftly through a cloud which quickly became a billowy carpet receding beneath me.

Turning from the scene below I watched my altimeter—4000 . . . 4500 . . . 5000. The needle was moving too quickly. I glanced at my rate-of-climb meter: 1200 feet per minute. That was too fast. To build up too high an ascent speed at low altitude could mean disaster hours from now. As the balloon rose through the tropopause it would increase its speed. And if it ascended too quickly into the rarefied atmosphere where the helium would rapidly expand I would be unable to valve off all of the excess gas. With too much helium inside, the polyethylene bag would swell like an overfilled toy balloon and burst. Establishing the correct ascent rate now, while still close to the earth, was vital.

"Hello N-C-A Three One," I called to Winzen on the VHF radio. "This is N-C-A Three Eight. I'm going to valve off a little gas here until I slow down to 900 feet a minute." I tried to sound cool and businesslike, but I couldn't suppress adding:

"Otto, it's wonderful . . . like rising on an endless elevator."

"Roger on the valving," he called back. "But take it easy. Try opening the valve for ten seconds at five-minute intervals. That should check it. And keep the balloon in sight while you're valving. I'd like to know if it flutters or shows any other reaction while the valve is open."

"Wilco, Three One. I'm valving now . . . So far as I can see, there's no sign of an external reaction from the valving."

I held my finger tight over the strong spring switch that triggered a three-foot electric motor-driven valve at the top of the balloon. The valve opened like a huge camera shutter and stayed open as long as I pressed the switch, allowing some of the surging gas to escape.

"N-C-A Three One, this is Three Eight. Finished ten seconds of valving and no perceptible change in ascent rate. I'll wait five minutes and do it again."

I turned busily to other jobs. Gildenberg and I were vitally interested in getting a precise record of the Man High system's oscillation as it rose to altitude, because we hoped some day to help someone design a balloon-borne telescopic observatory that would be capable of seeing Mars in fine detail. To do this, we knew that we would have to have a full record of the oscillations and movements of the Man High system, for we would have to use this as a guide in designing a capsule and balloon system that would remain steady long enough to provide a firm platform for a big telescope. With one hand I flicked on my Midgetape tape recorder to dictate the time intervals and the kinds of oscillation as the capsule spun lazily under its 60-foot suspension lines. With my other hand I reached for the Cinekodak movie camera to record not only the rotation but the brightness and color of the sky at 10,000 feet and at each 10,000-foot interval above. I paused to check my instruments, then dropped the camera to scribble observations on a note pad attached to a clipboard on my knee, then pressed again on the valve switch.

For the next thirty minutes I had no more time for lyric reflection on the beauties of the world below or the sky around me. But I had seen this part of the atmosphere countless times while flying, and it was no different today.

By 30,000 feet the loss of gas from valving had slowed the balloon to a safer 1000 feet-per-minute ascent, a gentle ten-mile-an-hour flight straight up. Except for the crystalline brightness of the sky, it was like rising smoothly from the depths of a bottomless pool of water. But in this pool the darkness lurked above and the bright light of life lay below. Through the mirror I could see the shimmering sunlit balloon stand out sharply against the characteristic deep blue of the high altitude sky. With each foot of the ascent the blue sky color darkened, rolling back to the horizon all around to be engulfed by the blackness of space.

Now I was rising into the tropopause, the region of the high-speed jet streams. Gildenberg had told me to expect 60-mile-an-hour winds here. And I watched intently as I approached 48,000 feet to see if the balloon would be shoved over on its side as Kittinger's had been on the first Man High flight. But I neither saw nor felt a sudden change of direction or sensation of speed. The balloon had edged into the stream so smoothly that it was unbothered, becoming simply another piece of cosmic dust drifting in the strong current, as much a part of the wind as the lightest flotsam. It was speeding to the east, carrying me toward Lake Michigan. As I passed through the stream, a slower,

westward wind current gently took hold and the balloon
began to drift back again, toward the mountains of
Montana.

I checked my capsule pressure gauge on the instrument
panel. The gondola was built so that it would automatically
maintain a pressure equal to air pressure at 25,000 feet
altitude, comfortable and safe when enriched with oxygen
as mine was. The gauge showed an equivalent of 25,000
feet, but I thought I detected an almost imperceptible drop
in pressure.

"N-C-A Three One, this is Three Eight."

"Go ahead, Three Eight."

"My capsule pressure looks like it might be dropping
very slowly. I'm not sure yet, but the gauge shows just a
slight drop." It was better to get at the problem now, even
though it might not develop, than to wait for stronger confirmation in the form of a big loss of pressure.

"Three Eight, this is Three One." I recognized Archibald's voice on the radio. "Keep an eye on the pressure for
any big change. It might hold steady. But if it drops any
more you can always cut off the automatic pressure-control
system and shift to manual."

"Roger, Three One." By opening a valve to let more compressed oxygen into the capsule from the liquid oxygen
tanks outside, I could manually control the capsule pressure. I decided to wait until the pressure loss was more
pronounced.

"Three Eight," the radio blared again. It was Otto calling. During the hours to follow he would be my constant
touchstone to reality, a radio voice that would become so
familiar to me that I would even begin to feel that Winzen
was in the capsule beside me rather than in his control van
on the ground.

"We are going off the air for about a half hour now. You are drifting west at about five miles an hour. To stay ahead of you, we're going to leave the mine area and move up to Brainerd, about 30 miles northwest of here. We'll stop at the Brainerd airport and follow you from there. Meanwhile the C-47 is airborne. He will track you while we're moving. If you need anything, call him."

"Roger, Three One," I called. Now I would have an uninterrupted half hour in which to enjoy my view of earth and sky and concentrate on the photographs and tape-recorded observations which radio conversation had interrupted.

Glancing into my split-view mirror I noted that the balloon no longer fluttered with air turbulence. It was at 65,000 feet now, well into the stratosphere where the rarefied air did not gust about erratically. But with this rare atmosphere came an intense cold and I began to feel it. Irritatedly, I rubbed my chilled hands together. The fingers had become so cold they fumbled clumsily as I opened the Cinekodak to change film. Paradoxically, my dry-ice pack, snugly wrapped around the upper hemisphere of the gondola to keep me cool on the ground, was still working, adding to the chill of the stratosphere. I could see the wispy vapors produced by evaporating dry ice drifting past the portholes.

Looking down on the earth below, I watched the crisp, saturated dark brown earth of plowed fields and the cool, shaded green of the thick Minnesota forest fade perceptibly, as if bright colors oozing from tubes of paint were mixing with an invisible chemical that slowly robbed them of their primary brilliance and left them as washed-out pastels. The neat geometry of plowed fields and squared border lines remained in miniature, but their colors lost contrast and merged into patches of blotched dull green and brown.

Above me the sky was now totally dark in contrast to the bright sunlight that played upon the balloon and penetrated the shadows inside the capsule.

I looked at my standard high-altitude altimeter: 75,000 feet. It had almost reached its limit and probably would work accurately no longer. Beside it was the face of another altimeter, especially designed by Wallace and Tiernan to register altitudes correctly from 65,000 up to 150,000 feet. I would follow my ascent from now on with the Wallace and Tiernan gauge. Outside the capsule, lashed to the undercarriage, was a third gauge of altitude, a radio beacon whose coded signal gave Vern Baumgartner in the control van a periodic reading on my altitude.

The standard Air Force altimeter, working on a sensitive pressure bulb like a barometer, had now passed beyond the region in which it could sense the change of pressure with altitude. My rate-of-climb indicator, built on the same principle, also had stopped sensing change. So to check my vertical speed, I timed the altitude increase on the Wallace and Tiernan gauge.

It was 1200 feet a minute. Too fast again.

"N-C-A Three One, this is Three Eight. Do you read me? Over?"

I hoped the van had arrived at Brainerd and was listening for me.

"Three Eight, this is Three One. We just set up here at Brainerd airport. Go ahead. Over."

I could imagine the big van followed by its improbable caravan of trucks, station wagons, and cars spread out along the grass-covered country airfield. If the people down there followed my old practice in chasing balloons, most of them probably were lying stretched out in the grass, faces up, shading their eyes from the sun and straining to see the sunlit balloon overhead.

"Three One. I've picked up ascent again. It's 1200 feet per minute. I'm going to start valving to slow it down."

"Three Eight, this is Three One." It was Winzen. "That's much too fast for your altitude. You'd better start valving immediately. Open the valve for two minutes at a time until you've cut the ascent to 800 or 900 feet a minute."

"Roger, Three One. I'm valving now."

"Three Eight. Please keep the balloon in sight and tell me how it looks. You'll pass 82,000 feet in a few minutes. At that altitude, it should be exactly half full."

The altimeter needle turned steadily, indicating I still was climbing too fast. As it swept past 82,000 I looked sharply into the split mirror. The balloon still was not half full. In a rising balloon, the helium volume doubles every 18,000 feet, so that at 18,000 feet the bag is twice as swollen as at sea level; at 36,000 feet it is four times as swollen; at 54,000 it is eight times as swollen, and so on upwards. At 82,000 it should have expanded to exactly half of its 200-foot diameter, and at 100,000 feet it should be completely filled out.

"Three One. This is Three Eight. There's something funny here. I've just passed 82,000 feet and the balloon is not half full. Is there something wrong with this Wallace and Tiernan altimeter?"

"Three Eight," Otto called back. "The altimeter should read correctly. It was calibrated by the National Bureau of Standards. What's your rate of ascent now?"

"Near as I can make out from timing the altimeter, it's coming down a little. I'm going to valve some more. It's just under 1100 feet per minute now."

"Roger, Three Eight."

Steadily the altimeter crept upwards. At 90,000 feet I called again.

"The balloon is barely half full now and the altimeter reads 90,000. Could that be right?"

"Wait one minute, Three Eight." It was Vern Baumgartner's voice on the radio. "I'm checking your altitude on the radio beacon right now." He paused. "Three Eight. The radio beacon shows you right at 82,000 feet now."

I studied the instrument panel again. The altimeter now read 91,000 and still climbing. Glancing aside, I checked the capsule pressure gauge. It was falling now. The automatic-pressure system was not working properly.

"Three One. Forget the altitude problem for a minute, Vern, and tell Arch that my capsule pressure is falling again." If I permitted the pressure to drop too low I would be in serious trouble.

"Three Eight," Archibald called. "If you think the pressure-control system isn't holding up, you'd better seal it off and go on to manual control now."

"Roger, Arch," I called. "I'll switch to manual. The automatic system obviously isn't working right."

"Three Eight," Otto called. "What's your indicated altitude on the Wallace and Tiernan now?"

I looked at the altimeter gauge. Now I knew it was way off.

"Otto, it reads 105,000 feet. That must be wrong."

"How full is the balloon?"

"It's about three-fourths inflated. The altimeter can't be right."

I half smiled at my eagerness to prove the error of the altimeter. For two years I had hoped to ascend one day above 100,000 feet, not for the sake of a record, but because that was the region I wanted to explore. Now that I was up and my altimeter showed me to be above that mark, I refused to believe it. But simple mathematics told me that the unexpanded state of the balloon proved I had not yet reached 100,000.

There was a short pause before Winzen's voice came through the radio again.

"You are right, Dave. The altimeter is off. Doctor Johnson just came into the van and we decided the Bureau of Standards made a mistake when they calibrated it. We'll have to keep you informed of exact altitude from the radio beacon. But you can use the Wallace and Tiernan to check your rate of ascent. Will you check that now, please?"

"Roger," I called. For one minute I watched the altimeter, checking it against my wrist chronometer. "We can breathe easier now, Otto. Ascent rate is down to 800 feet a minute. I hope we can believe that."

I looked through the mirror at the balloon overhead. It was now very nearly full, a swollen ball 200 feet wide. Its bulbous sides were pinched by fiberglass bands so that it looked like a transparent peeled orange. Each of the seventy bands running down the sides of the balloon was a load carrier, strong enough to hold 500 pounds. Together they would support 35,000 pounds, far more than enough to hold the 1712 pounds of parachute equipment, gondola, and man suspended from them.

"I'm pretty close to the top now, Otto," I called. "The balloon is almost full and my rate of ascent has dropped off sharply."

The ascent dropped to an agonizingly slow speed. I watched the altimeter, now reading 127,000 feet, to see when its needle would stop rising. But it still edged upwards.

In my hands, still almost numb with cold, I held an opened movie camera. Before reaching ceiling altitude, I had to change film and shoot another in the every 10,000-foot series. Shifting eyes from camera to altimeter to camera to pressure gauge to camera, I worked carefully to load a new spool of film. If my numbed fingers slipped and the spool fell to the floor of the cramping capsule, it might take fifteen minutes of strained maneuvering in the confining capsule to retrieve it. And I could not afford to waste minutes on mistakes.

The altimeter faltered, then stopped. I noted the time: 11:40. It had taken me two hours and eighteen minutes to bump against the earth's ceiling. Slowly the needle dropped, then rose again. The balloon was gently bouncing like a basketball being dribbled in slow motion in an upside-down world. It had ascended as high as it would go.

My radio earphones crackled.

"N-C-A Three Eight, this is Three One." Otto's voice sounded jubilant. "The radio beacon altitude is 102,000 feet, I repeat, 102,000 feet. Congratulations, Dave. That's a record."

Too excited to care about the hazards of living where no man had tarried before, I looked around me. The earth's familiar blue atmosphere was easily discernible around the entire horizon. If you consider an arc drawn from the eastern horizon up through the sky overhead and down to the western horizon as 180 degrees, the band of blue that represents the sky to an earthbound viewer reached up about ten degrees all around. It was fuzzily stratified within that ten degrees, beginning at the horizon with a washed out whiteness and gradually changing to pale blue that grew ever deeper until it merged with the intensely deep but dark bluish purple of space. This was the earth and its atmosphere as the pilots of the X-15 would see it during their searing, hot glide down from 100 miles up.

Aiming my spot photometer at the horizon and then edging it up through the bands of blue, I read the exact light brightness as it faded into the darkness above. And then with a finely calculated color chart I tried to match the colors of the atmosphere as seen from its outer rim. The color samples, provided by Dr. Stakutis of the Air Force Cambridge Research Center, included every perceived shade of color man can reproduce in pigment. But not one of them could match the strange blue-purple color my eyes beheld now at the atmosphere's outermost edge.

Where the atmosphere merged with the colorless blackness of space, the sky was so heavily saturated with this blue-purple color that it was inescapable, yet its intensity was so low that it was hard to comprehend, like a musical note which is beautifully vibrant but so high that it lies almost beyond the ear's ability to hear, leaving you certain of its brilliance but unsure whether you actually heard it or dreamed of its beauty.

Taking in the entire panorama through my portholes, I had the feeling that I was suspended high above a giant dish. Below me was the warmly lit earth with clouds hugging close to its surface, and far away in every direction was its rim of atmosphere, etched against a dark sky like the moon's rim in the night. I could see 400 miles in every direction and gaze upon a half-million square miles of the earth below.

Along the horizon a faint curve told me that the earth is a globe. But instead of making the planet seem smaller, my twenty-mile-high vantage point powerfully emphasized its incomprehensible enormity. I felt puny and humbled by the realization that although I could look 400 miles in any direction, I was only barely able to perceive the roundness of our planet. If man had not already discovered that the earth is round, I probably would have thought the curvature I saw was just an optical trick.

On the flattened rim of the globe I could make out the shadowy lines of Lake Michigan far to the east. It stood out as a dark and cloudless patch in a sea of white haziness. Slightly south of me a narrow string of shining water, the broad Mississippi River, sliced between Minneapolis and St. Paul and trickled down through Wisconsin.

I looked all around, drinking the huge expanse in great gulps with my eyes. To the southeast, just along the horizon's rim, an indistinct puffiness softened the sharp edge of the earth and trailed with it as far west as I could see. It was clearly an enormous cloud formation, but it was so far away I could not distinguish its structure or its nature. Much later I would know its nature all too well.

Far beneath me the ground crew was setting up a portable six-inch telescope beside the communications van.

Vern Baumgartner called.

"N-C-A Three Eight. Otto has you in the telescope now. He says the balloon looks completely full and he can see every gore of it standing out in the sunshine. From here it looks like you are standing still."

"Feels like it to me, too Vern," I replied. "There is absolutely no sensation of motion here."

"I wish I had your view," he quipped. "Can you give us a rundown on your checkoff list now? It's time for your two o'clock report."

"Roger, Vern." I turned to the dials of my instrument panel and one by one began the arduous tasks of technically checking the comfort and safety of the capsule. Every hour during the flight I would have to go down the complete check list and every half-hour I would have to give an abbreviated check, listing the most important items. Already I was becoming slightly annoyed by these regular breaks in my schedule, for they robbed me of time that I could have spent with the spot photometer or with the cameras. I began to feel as if we were spending too much time talking and not enough time acting. But the check list was essential. The ground party had to know what the instruments said in order to know surely how I fared.

Oxygen. Still almost full: 4.2 liters left out of 5 liters aboard. Good. No chance of repeating the touch-and-go Kittinger problem. Carbon dioxide: 1 per cent. Okay. It can go up to 3 per cent without danger. More than that and I might be in serious trouble. Capsule pressure: still dropping. I must maintain the safe pressure of 25,000 feet. Air temperature around me: 55 degrees. Wonderfully comfortable now. No longer bitter cold and numbing. But it's climbing. I'll turn on the air cooler now. I'll have to watch that temperature closely this afternoon when the sun has had a good chance to warm the capsule up. Surface temperature of the capsule on the sunny side must be nearly 200 degrees now. But it's well below freezing on the shady side.

Damn. Now the portholes are clouding over. Spots of moisture growing between the double layers of plexiglass. If it builds up much more I won't be able to see a thing.

Outside, the sun was a brilliant blue-white ball suspended in a dark sky, an eye-searing globe of intensely hot gas 100 million miles away. It was strange to see it thus, hanging in blackness by itself, not lighting the sky around it as it seems to do from the earth. Like an artist measuring an object for perspective, I held a thumb up in my line of sight so that it just barely blotted out the intense white fireball. Dr. Jack Evans of Sacramento Peak Observatory had asked me to look for visible evidence of the sun's corona, the crown of incredibly hot hydrogen gas that spreads far into space around the solar ball. But I saw nothing except the darkness of space tightly gripping the sun on all sides. There was no evidence of visible light or sky brightness beyond its rim. Then as my eyes searched in the void between the sun and the earth's curving surface, they came upon something never before seen by man. I felt a tingle of thrill at this first discovery. Around me, well above the haze layer of the atmosphere and close to the curtain of darkness above, was a procession of paper-thin sharp bands of yellow-brown etched against the deepening blue of the sky. I could not detect their altitude since I had no way of knowing whether they were close to me or far away. Their presence in the upper atmosphere had been theorized by Dr. Duntley of Scripps and Major Brennan of the Cambridge Research Center. Neither knew for certain what caused the bands, but I guessed they were thin bands of dust shot into the outer limits of the atmosphere by violent storms, volcanoes, and perhaps, in part, atomic explosions.

I flipped on my tape recorder to transcribe the observation, then reached for the cameras to record the faint yellow-brown strata. It would be exciting later to show photographs of the dust bands to Duntley and Brennan. But the lines were so thin and so pale that I feared they would not register on the film. Weeks later I learned they did not.

It was three o'clock. Time for another report. And another job to do.

A high-flying F-89 had been dispatched to crisscross the sky 70,000 feet below me. The Air Force wanted to know how clearly visible the jet con trails of the Scorpion would be when viewed from 100,000 feet. For an hour I carefully scanned the scene below, pausing occasionally to shoot pictures, to check the capsule instruments, and to take light-brightness readings. But the visual search was in vain.

"He's making a vapor trail right below you now," Otto called after nearly an hour. "It's not a very good day for vapor and the trail is pretty weak. But if you can see it at all you should be able to see it now."

. I looked intently. But below I saw nothing but puffy clouds and the dim outline of Minnesota farmland. The experiment was inconclusive.

Time for the four o'clock check list.

I shifted in the springy nylon seat, arching my back, and felt the cramping tug of the tight-fitting pressure suit against crotch and shoulders. Around my neck the clammy rubber pressure seal inside the suit rubbed against tender skin as I lifted my head to scan the instrument panel. It was getting warmer; 74 degrees now, just below the borderline of real discomfort. Perspiration soaked my long cotton underwear, uncomfortably sticky against my skin.

Not worrisome yet, though, I thought. It probably will go up to 80 or so before the afternoon is over, but I can stand that without trouble until sunset. Still, the water-can cooler should be keeping the temperature lower than this. It worked better in the pressure chamber at Wright Field.

Oxygen. Still over four liters. That's fine. Capsule pressure. Still holding at 380 milibars, equal to 25,000 feet. As long as I'm holding that level manually I'll have to keep an eye on it.

With difficulty I extracted the CO_2 analysis kit from its clamp beside my right foot and worked for two minutes on the carbon dioxide reading.

Still holding at slightly under 1 per cent. Everything

under control there, I thought. Altitude: the Wallace and Tiernan reads 132,000 feet. That must be 98,000 feet in real altitude. I'd better ballast a little after the check-list report.

With my right foot I hit the pedal-type switch that turned on my radio transmitter and began reading the check items to Baumgartner in the same numbered code we had used on Joe's flight.

"Thanks, Three Eight," he replied. "You figured your altitude about right. I get just 98,000 feet from the radio beacon."

"Roger, Three One. I'm going to experiment with dribbling some ballast now to see how well I can control this thing."

On the undercarriage outside the gondola was a box of iron dust which opened to allow a thin trickle to drain away whenever I touched a control switch. I tugged the switch now, tentatively letting small driblets of finely ground metal pour out to lighten the load under the balloon. Slowly, almost imperceptibly, the balloon rose as the weight drained away. Then it settled again. Carefully I drained away more of the iron dust, trying to achieve a balance so I could float at a steady altitude with no movement up or down.

My preoccupation with the delicate ballasting operation was interrupted by the radio. Throughout the day it seemed that every time I became immersed in an observation or an experiment, the ground radio interrupted. Later I would be thankful for this constant link to reality. But now it was annoying.

"Three Eight, this is Three One." The voice was Winzen's. "We are going to shift our base camp again and will be off the air for a while. We're moving to Detroit Lakes, about an hour from here. But we'll stop in a half hour and check in with you . . ."

I was delighted. I could count on a full hour without interruption. Attached to the clipboard on my knee was a neatly penned schedule I had prepared long before flight time to regulate the amount of time I devoted to any one observation during the flight. By my preset schedule, it was now time to search the darkness above for visible stars. Although the earth still was bathed in full afternoon sunlight, I expected to see some of the brighter stars in the black heavens above. But so far I had seen none. Mercury and Venus, both relatively close to the sun, should have been the two brightest objects visible. But there was nothing. Only the void. Squinting slightly, I placed my right eye over the magnifying eyepiece of the telescope and touched the switch that swept its reflecting mirror in a wide arc across the sky. But even with magnification there was no sign of stars or planets.

Later I understood why. The Man High capsule was designed and painted in such a way that it captured a maximum of reflected light from the earth and clouds below. This light entered the portholes and bounced from the light-colored hemisphere, diffusing inside the capsule. As a result, my eyes were every bit as accustomed to daylight as they would be if I had remained on the ground. Consequently, when I looked for stars I did so with daylight eyes, not with eyes adapted to the dark. Although I was suspended in a dark sky, the capsule that protected me was a sealed can full of daylight, and even the brightest stars in the heavens were invisible to me.

Turning aside from the fruitless star search I looked once more to the west and for the first time saw the full scope of the line of clouds that had given the earth its fuzzy edge hours before. It was a startlingly beautiful sight, a seemingly endless bank of cumulo-nimbus clouds making a puffy white cushion between the earth and sky and reflecting a sharp, cottony whiteness against shadowy folds. The upholstered softness of the cloud formation was soothing to look upon. Atop the puffy clouds, swirling, anvil-shaped chimneys reached upward and bent over, like dozens of tiny fingers beckoning me westward.

I longed to get closer to the cloud formation for a more detailed look. Little did I know that before I was through I would long to escape this thing of beauty. For this was the storm front which, unbeknownst to me, had caused Duke Gildenberg's curious reticence of the night before. But now I looked on it as a thing of beauty and scientific interest, not a source of fear.

I looked back at my instrument panel.

Still holding at about 98,000 feet, I noted. Let's see . . . 4:25 now and I've been up since 9:22 this morning. Seven hours. Been sitting in here since ten o'clock last night. That's eighteen and a half hours.

For the first time, the sense of hours spent in this one position focused my attention on the muscles of back and legs. Both were beginning to ache, but I had not been aware of the feeling before, I stretched, then half stood in a bent-forward crouch with my hard plastic helmet rubbing against the close wall of the capsule.

There, that's better, I thought as I dropped back into the net seat. But it's getting damned hot in here.

I glanced at the temperature gauge, it was up to 76 degrees now. A fine line between 74 and 76 seemed to make all the difference in the world. The perspiration that soaked my underwear felt hot against my skin. I opened the zippers of my pressure suit and stuck the cabin cooler's air hose inside, playing it over accessible skin and trying to force the nozzle between suit and body to reach my overheated back. It was a crude system, but it helped to dry my underclothes and cool my skin at the same time.

Since reaching peak altitude, the capsule had been rotating slowly with the giant balloon, very gently turning first one way then the other. It was not disturbing, but whenever I moved sharply within the capsule it bounced like a weight on a soft spring, causing a vibration to ascend through the suspension system to the balloon and back again. By peering through the eyepiece of the telescope and focusing on the cloud bank to the west, I could time the rotation perfectly, watching the cloud bank sweep first in one direction, then the other. I dictated the timed rotations into the Midgetape. This would be valuable data for designers and astronomers who will launch balloon-borne telescopes in the future. The more they know about the nature and causes of the rotation, the better they will be able to design a stable high-altitude observatory.

Once again the radio interrupted. It was 4:30. Just Vern checking the radio, I thought.

"N-C-A Three Eight, this is Three One. Over." It was Winzen.

Rather than move my eye from the telescope eyepiece, I tapped the transmitter foot switch twice, rapidly, to signal that I was listening. The two taps would make a double click in the van receiver.

"Three Eight. Please drop whatever you're doing if you can," Otto called. "We've got a problem."

I wondered idly if the van had had an accident on the road to Detroit Lakes, where Otto had planned to set up operations until after dark.

"Roger, Three One," I replied. "What is it?"

"Dave, the heart and respiration signals are completely gone. All we get on the high-frequency radio channel is an occasional beep. So far we haven't been able to figure out what's wrong."

Quickly I checked my channel-selector switches. Everything was okay.

"No malfunction that I can find at this end, Otto," I told him. "If you want, I can include my pulse and respiration rates in the regular hourly checkoff."

"That's not the problem, Dave," he called. "We were using that radio as a high-frequency beacon to keep track of your position. Also it was the only back-up radio you had."

"It doesn't bother me if it doesn't worry you," I said. "We've still got the VHF voice radio that we're using now."

"I know," Otto replied, "but that's getting frisky, too. The frequency had been shifting slightly. Vern is afraid that it might go out sooner or later. That would leave you with no communications at all."

A possibility of a night alone far above the earth with no communications; and already the certainty that Stapp could no longer check my physical well-being by listening to my heart and respiration signals?

"What does Colonel Stapp think?" I asked.

The colonel's voice, squeezed and high-pitched by the radio, came on:

"I'm going to leave it up to you, Dave," he said. "Do you want to come down now rather than risk it?"

Otto came on again.

"You understand that you will have to see it through the night alone if the radio fails?" he asked.

They were asking me if I wanted to come down, to land before the flight was half-finished. Why? Because they might lose me during the night. But in the morning they shouldn't have too much trouble locating me again. That would be no great problem. There were two airplanes, the veteran C-47 and a light plane tracking me visually now. They would find me tomorrow. Even if they did not find me, the question was academic unless I crashed and needed help. I was essentially alone anyway. The absence or presence of a radio did not make me any more or less alone. As long as the flight went smoothly, the radio served only to reassure the ground crew. The only inconvenience its absence would cause me would be the added chore of writing my hourly pilot reports instead of reading them over the radio.

Was there another reason to consider ending the flight now? Yes. Stapp, deprived of the sound of my heartbeat and breathing would have no way of knowing my physical condition if my VHF radio broke down. Even with the VHF, if anything happened that left me unable to report my condition, the crew on the ground could go blissfully through the night with no knowledge of the trouble. I could be in bad shape and they wouldn't know it until they cut me down in the morning. Should I end the flight and descend now?

If I wanted to search for reasons to quit, I could have found them. The heat had built up to the point where I was having difficulty tolerating it. And I was tired. I had not slept, other than to cat-nap, since the afternoon before, almost twenty-four hours. Already I felt the familiar old pain in my knee. And my back ached, probably from slumping in the seat all day. But so far none of these problems had even approached becoming insurmountable.

On the positive side, there was nothing wrong with the balloon. Before take-off I had half feared the possibility of a leaky balloon. With such a huge expanse of paper-thin plastic, it would not have been too surprising to find a leak in the great bag. But there were none and I was elated. It had held at ceiling altitude all afternoon and it was holding now. There was no doubt in my mind that it would go on performing perfectly through the night. The weather still looked good. And the capsule was holding up well despite the heat. It would cool quickly when the sun dropped below the horizon.

I had much left to do. The night sky; the stars; the simple physical and psychological fact of remaining confined and alone in space; these were urgent observations. I had planned them for two years. I was profoundly grateful that they had enough confidence in me to ask if I wanted to go on.

"Hello, Colonel Stapp. And Otto." I wanted them both to hear. "With your permission, I'm staying up here. There's nothing, repeat, nothing wrong with the system. If you can stand the doubt, we'll make it through the night."

"Very well, Dave. Permission granted." It was Colonel Stapp. His voice, although pinched by the radio, sounded relieved. He had been no more anxious to end the flight than I.

The time passed quickly as I returned to the job of looking at the strange world around me.

Six o'clock now and still no sign of the stars. Although I flew into darkness before noon, I will have to wait until darkness envelops the earth before my capsule will be drained of its daylight to allow me a glimpse of the heavens. Temperature is rising; 77 degrees now. I can feel its effect and even hear it as I dictate in a sluggish, dull voice to the tape recorder. As I talk, I know that I am not speaking crisply, normally. Ideas form fuzzily and flow sporadically from a tongue that has trouble finding words. Damned nuisance to record everything. I'm getting tired. Got to record the lens setting for the movies I just made. Let's see. Turn on the recorder.

"Uh . . . three horizon pictures panned vertically . . . Oh, hell . . .

"Those last pictures . . . uh . . . didn't count. We didn't . . . uh . . . have any film in the camera . . .

"The . . . uh . . . temperature . . . is 63 degrees on the instrument panel . . . that doesn't really count there . . . it's, uh, 77 degrees, so it's very warm in here . . ."

But it's late afternoon and the sun should set soon. Why hasn't it begun to cool off? Better get busy and try to forget it. Sunset ought to be about an hour and a half from now. I'll dictate some more.

"Uh . . . this is . . . 6:15 . . . I'm facing east, directly east, directly to the east, and it's getting fairly close to sum . . . uh . . . to sunset. The . . . uh . . . nature of the horizon and the band just above it is interes . . . intensely interesting. One gets almost a stratified effect observing it, in the region where it transfers from the characteristic dark violet of the zenith to the pink white of just above the horizon . . ."

There that wasn't so bad. I can make reasonably coherent observations in spite of the heat.

I wiggled uncomfortably in the net seat and continued: "Since all of the higher clouds have disappeared to the east, one can see it truly as a round globe, an enormous curved globe stretching out . . . and . . . uh . . . just . . . uh . . . a whole area without any clouds at all. Just a few patchy ones here and there . . ."

Let's see now. Hmn. Capsule pressure is rising a little bit. I'd better bring it down. Better tell the tape recorder, then let the people on the ground know.

"N-C-A Three One, this is N-C-A Three Eight. Over."

"Go ahead, Three Eight," Otto replied.

"Uh . . . I'm bringing the temperature . . . uh . . . that's not right . . . no, the pressure down to . . . let's see . . . from 440 to 400 milibars.

"It's just a little bit too warm in here, Otto, but it should start cooling off very shortly."

There was a pause, then my receiver buzzed.

"Three Eight, this is Colonel Stapp."

"Go ahead, Colonel," I called.

"Dave, when was the last time you ate?"

For a moment I wondered what was on his mind. Then I realized.

"I'm almost ashamed to tell you, Colonel Stapp. I've been so darned fascinated all day that I didn't recognize it myself until you just mentioned it. I haven't eaten a thing since we got into the pit this morning. That's when I ate my last sandwich."

"I thought so," Stapp said. I could hear him chuckle into the microphone. "Your voice is sluggish and you know as well as I do that you're blood sugar is probably way down. You'd better eat a candy bar."

"Wilco, sir. Right now."

I reached into the plastic food bag before me and pulled out a chocolate bar. Somehow the thought of food had never crossed my mind. During the ride from Minneapolis to Crosby I had eaten my sandwiches because I was afraid they would spoil if I left them uneaten too long. But from the moment of take-off my mind had been so totally bent to the jobs at hand and the fascinating sights around me that hunger simply had not come through. I still was not hungry. But it was obvious from my sluggishness that I needed a source of energy.

As I munched the chocolate, I thought of the heat again. Inside my helmet, with its pressure liner pulled tightly around my face and ears and neck, the dampness of perspiration was annoyingly cloying. But still it was tolerable, endurable, like an itch that is annoying and will not go away, but you know that if you can remember not to scratch, it will not be so bothersome. But I knew that it was cutting into my feeling of alertness, my efficiency, and I resented it because it robbed my attention.

Soon my eyes were totally absorbed by the most startling sight they ever have seen. Unless I some day fly far into space I doubt that I will find a sight to equal the panoply of constantly changing color that enveloped the earth for an hour before sunset.

To the west of me the sun still perched as a brilliant white ball above the earth, separated from the white haze of the horizon by a narrow band of dark space. But to the east, the direction the capsule now faced, the sun already had set for the people below. They were in semidarkness. The ground had a formless slate-gray appearance, like a flat rock in shadow at the foot of a hill. But up the hill, in the sky above this darkened earth, the atmosphere glowed with the colors excited by the lingering light of the sun.

Paradoxically, I was still suspended in the full light of the sun, and to my back, somewhere over Colorado and the Dakotas, it still bathed the earth. But in front of me, over Lake Michigan, Wisconsin, and Minnesota, it was setting. And a curious reversal of night and day met my eyes. High in the atmosphere, where the sun still shot its rays, the ever deepening blue sky was acquiring a greenish, sunset tinge. But below it, closer to the earth, was a giant demarcation line which looked like a faded rainbow arching from south to north across the eastern horizon. And beneath the line was the darkness of night covering the earth below. The daylit sky was above, the darkened sky below. And as the sunset progressed, the rainbow arch rose ever higher, drawing with it a curtain of blackness.

Where the darkness had not yet fallen, the changing sunlight majestically shifted its colors through the atmosphere, deepening here to a fiery red, fading there to a salmon pink, then to a pale yellow. Above the slowly changing colors was a layer of blue so clear that it was as if someone had lifted a veil from an ordinary blue sky to leave it polished and bright and clean with no scattered light to diffuse it.

For a full hour I watched in fascination, pausing every few minutes to shoot color pictures and to describe what I saw to my tape recorder and to the ground crew. Then as I listened to the van radio acknowledging one of my messages, I stood up to contribute a specimen to one of Archibald's plastic urine bottles. And as I did so, my earphones went dead.

Oh, damn it, I thought. Now the VHF is out. I was afraid it might go, but not without warning like this.

I checked my lip mike to see if it had tugged loose from its mooring on my helmet, but it was as it should have been. Then carefully I began checking each of the connections leading into and out of the transmitter and receiver. Suddenly I slumped back into the net seat and laughed uncontrollably in rolling gales that would have rocked a passing angel. In standing up to offer that mundane contribution to science, I had simply pulled my earphones plugs loose from their socket. A simple flip of the wrist to plug in the set put me back in business.

Below me now I could see the massive cloud system that had caught my attention earlier in the afternoon. It offered a fantastic sight as the thunderheads began to pick up the last glowing red rays of the sun, casting red silhouettes like forges before the glowing heat of a furnace. The clouds, probably 45,000 feet below me, were themselves another 50,000 feet above the earth, and this halfway reference gave me, for the first time, a true feeling for the enormous height at which my capsule was floating. I still had no cause to fear these clouds so far below.

Far to the west now, the great white ball of sun was dipping into the edge of the horizon, taking on a tinge of yellow before it began to disappear behind the horizon line of clouds. I timed its progression with my chronometer, noting to the split second when it first touched the horizon, when it was half set, and when the last trace of the fireball disappeared. At the same time I hastily shifted my Cinekodak and Nikon cameras to capture the day's end on film.

By 9 P.M. only a thin and short red crescent of afterglow remained. It held above the gray curve of the western horizon for an hour to show me where the sun had set.

As I looked at the glowing crescent an occasional faded flash of lightning cast a dim glow within the clouds. But far overhead was a more entrancing sight.

I had been so enthralled with the sunset that I had not noticed when the stars first became visible. But now I could see them, a sky full of them, shining as steady bright lights, not twinkling and pulsing through a heavy atmosphere as you see them on earth.

Close behind the setting sun trailed Venus, earth's closest neighbor and most earthlike of all the planets. I picked her up just a few degrees above the horizon and watched for sixteen minutes as she set in the wake of the sun. Her plunge below the horizon was almost as spectacular.

From my vantage point far above the earth, I was watching the setting planet through a double thickness of atmosphere, just as you look through two thicknesses when you peer through the curving side of a drinking glass. This led to a rainbow effect as the bright planet's light passed through the bands of air. It twinkled slowly in brilliant colors, each holding for about a second, then shifting suddenly to another: first green, then red, then yellow, as if a giant stage-light color filter turned slowly between Venus and my eyes.

Next came Jupiter, a far larger planet. But it did not give the astral color display that Venus had offered. Instantly I wondered if my position in the sky had changed radically between the two observations. I checked the altimeter. Its needle was turning downward. I was losing altitude.

I had expected to drop somewhat due to the contraction of helium from cooling when the sun went down. But now my descent appeared to be too fast.

"N-C-A Three One, this is Three Eight. I seem to be losing altitude a little too fast with this cooling effect. I'm going to drop 100 pounds of ballast to try to level off well above 80,000 feet."

"Roger, Three Eight," Otto called. "This is the first major ballast you've dropped, isn't it?"

"That is correct, Otto. I dribbled some iron dust a while ago, but this will be the first battery drop. I can't understand why I'm losing altitude quite so fast here."

Glancing into my mirror, I saw the reason for the rapid loss. The cloud system which had moved between me and the earth below had cut the balloon off from the earth's infra-red radiation, and as a result the helium in the balloon was cooling far faster than it would on a clear night. I tripped ballast switches number 1 and number 2, cutting away two 50-pound batteries which had been exhausted and were no longer useful except to be dropped. There was a gentle upward spring to the capsule as the weights fell away.

"Hello, Three One," I called. "Just ballasted batteries 1 and 2."

"Roger, Three Eight," Winzen replied. "By the way, how does this storm front between us look from your side?"

"A beautiful sight, Otto. I can see a little lightning in it here and there. When the sun set it picked up some wonderful colors."

"Gildenberg reports from Minneapolis that the same front moved very quickly through Denver this afternoon. He says it should move at about the same rate tonight, so you will be clear of it by morning."

"No sweat, Otto," I called. "I don't expect to descend any lower than 80,000 feet tonight, so there will be plenty of room between me and the storm. If I remember my meteorology lessons, thunderheads don't rise any higher than 45,000 or 50,000 feet."

"Right, Dave."

He paused for a moment, then came back on the radio.

"Dave, we're going off the air for a half hour now. We're packing up to move on to Fargo, North Dakota, for the night. We'll stop on the highway every half hour during the drive and contact you for your check list. Is there any information you need before I sign off?"

"No thanks, Otto. All I want right now is a chance to look at the stars."

I turned to the telescope. Jupiter was still far enough above the horizon for a sighting if I could only get it in the narrow field of the eyepiece. But to look was almost sickening. The balloon still was losing altitude slowly. And as it dropped it passed through varying eddies of air which turned it first one way, then the other. I could not find Jupiter in the eyepiece, but I did catch the untwinkling brilliance of the stars above as they moved across the field of view of the rotating telescope. And their appearance startled me. One normally does not think of the stars as being colorful, but only as points of light in the sky. Now I saw red stars burning a steady red, and blue stars were distinctly blue. They were not mere points of light, like blinking bulbs lighting a darkened street. They were untwinkling living, colorful objects with places of their own in the cosmos and depth in an endless universe.

But my awe of the universe quickly shifted to the awesome sight below me. It was a little after nine o'clock and now the storm that had moved in so rapidly had cut me off completely from the earth. It was a thing of great beauty, but I was thankful for my altitude, because it contained the seeds of destruction. Like a flashing neon display, the clouds were shot through with sporadic pulses of light that showed up a gorgeous pattern of puff and shadow. I timed the rapid pulsing of lightning; an impressive thirty strokes per minute. Quickly, I loaded my Nikon with Superanscochrome, fastest of the color films I had with me, and snapped pictures of the cloud formation with its impressive illumination.

As the night wore on I knew I would have more chance to watch this great storm front slide past beneath me, and I was glad for the opportunity to study it. Later, I knew, the moon would rise and light the clouds below so that I could watch them more closely than by the scattered light of their own electrical charges.

Thinking of the night ahead, I decided to get ready for it. The capsule had not begun to cool, as I hoped, when the sun went down. But I knew it was only a matter of time until it would become even chillier than it had been during the morning ascent. Almost reluctantly, I switched off my air blower. To leave it on now would cool my tiny cabin in the sky too quickly.

Altitude: now 87,000 feet, but still dropping slowly. Should I drop more ballast now to level off? I have already cut away my exhausted batteries. There is still some juice left in number 3 and number 4. To drop them now would cut into my power reserve. I'll have to be patient. This descent should stop pretty soon.

I was not worried, but the steady descent did concern me. In order to get "good seeing" with the telescope, I wanted to spend the night above 85,000 feet where there is virtually no water vapor in the atmosphere. I also wanted the balloon to hang steadily at one level above that altitude because ascent or descent seemed always to cause the maddening rotation that made telescope viewing impossible. Even more important to my comfort and safety, the capsule's temperature-control system was designed to function best above 85,000 feet. The paper and mylar insulation on the outside depended on a near vacuum to keep heat trapped within the capsule. If I descended to a denser level, the honeycombed layers of paper would fill with air that would conduct the cold to the skin of the gondola. The temperature outside now was 65 degrees below zero. I had no desire to have that chill creep into my space cabin.

Even so, the thought of a chill had some appeal. Capsule temperature had been over 75 degrees since 4:30 in the afternoon, and I knew it was steadily eating into my efficiency. I was soaked with sweat and recognized that I was bitterly tired. As I looked at my portholes, I cursed with a sense of futility. They had fogged over quickly when I turned the air blower off. My mind and body already were sapped with the effects of fatigue and persistent heat. Now a new barrier, the fogged portholes, stood between me and the observations I wanted to make. My attention wandered. My body ached. My mind cried for rest and relief. Each time I wanted to look out for a meaningful observation I had to fight through a heavy cloud of fatigue and grasp for the energy to wipe the moisture from a porthole. I felt as if I was rapidly aging, speeding through the years from thirty-five to senility in a few short hours.

As I dictated to the tape recorder, my voice stumbled over imperfectly formed ideas and the symptoms of heat stress poured out:

"It's 9:15 . . . uh . . . 66 . . . no 68 . . . uh . . . 76 degrees. I still feel hot as the dickens, understandably, from those temperatures . . . and . . . uh . . . sweaty. And my back aches like the deuce. Uh . . . there's something wrong with this chair this time. I've never noticed this before. I just feel like my back is going to break. I don't understand why. I must not be sitting up straight or something. I must be bending it too much, slouching over . . ."

I felt miserable. But if anyone had asked me if I wanted to get out I would have been appalled. I recognized my aches and feelings of frustration as symptoms of the frailty of my body, not as reasons to justify discouragement over floating alone high above the earth. It was frustrating and damnably uncomfortable, but instead of permitting dejection to take hold, I became even more determined to break through the futility, to submerge the aches and fight off the fatigue.

By ten o'clock my voice had gone from a sluggish drawl marked by mumbled words, to a speedy outpouring of hurried remarks, as if I suspected that I might be interrupted at any moment.

"At this point," I told the tape recorder, "my left knee is just giving me fits like it did a couple of times before. Umn. I just can't seem to get into a position where it is even halfway comfortable. I think I'm very thirsty—part of my trouble . . . I think I'm just tired more than anything . . ."

Periodically, Winzen called. I did not describe to him my fatigue. But he must have recognized it from the sound of my voice. I knew that he and Stapp and the others must be every bit as tired as I was, for they had been as tense and as sleepless. But at least they had room for movement. They could get up and walk. They could breathe fresh air. They were cool now in the darkness of night.

Irritated with the nagging rotation of the still-descending gondola, I lethargically wiped the moisture from one window and tried to observe the sky around me. But it was virtually impossible to hold anything in my field of view. Looking out only a single window, unable to shift my eyes to another porthole when the gondola swung around, I saw a panorama but I could never keep my eyes fixed on one part of the sky long enough to study it carefully. The balloon was still descending slowly. At 10:30 I dropped a now exhausted 50-pound battery pack to check it.

For a few minutes my interest perked up. Out of the single cleared window at 10:42, I saw the glorious tail of Mrkos' comet (1957d), flashing twice as long and twice as brilliantly as it does when seen from the earth. Like a flaming cosmic arrow hurtling over a fortress, it was poised over a glowing auroral display along the northern horizon. The aurora was a many-folded curtain of light in which each fold shot upwards like the beam of a searchlight tinted with a fire green. Under the bottom edge of the aurora was a strip of star-speckled sky separating the astral display from the earth's horizon.

But soon my attention shifted back to my own discomfort. The stresses of heat and fatigue were now so completely overriding my objective desire to make observations of the stars that I could no longer fend them off. At 11:30 I wearily called the van by radio.

"N-C-A Three One, this is Three Eight. I'm just too tired to go on for a while. With your permission, I think I'll try for a half hour's sleep."

Colonel Stapp was manning the radio in the van.

"Roger, Dave," he called. "Better to spend some time resting than fighting yourself. You'll be able to accomplish a lot more after some sleep."

"Thanks, Colonel," I replied.

"One other thing," Stapp added. "In case you haven't already done it, you'd better eat another candy bar to keep your blood sugar up."

I smiled. Once again I had forgotten food completely. My food store still included a can of peanuts, two full canned flight rations, and a package of candy bars. I had no interest in opening the flight rations for a full meal. So I munched two of the candy bars.

Then I hooked the faceplate to my helmet, letting it swing loose but fastened at the top so that I could simply reach up and snap it shut in case of emergency decompression while I slept. Before drifting into a light sleep, I mentally tossed and turned over the nagging thought that I was sacrificing valuable time which could be spent making observations. But then, the colonel was right. With a little sleep I should be better able to make observations later.

Just before drifting off to sleep I noticed the altimeter.

It was still dropping slowly. The standard Air Force altimeter which would not work at extremely high altitudes was now moving slightly down from its 85,000 foot peak.

I slept.

"N-C-A Three Eight . . . N-C-A Three Eight . . . N-C-A Three Eight . . . Do you read me? Do you read me? Do you read me?"

I was only dimly aware of a voice, sunken and far away, calling a familiar number. Groggily, I opened my eyes. The voice called on.

"N-C-A Three Eight . . . Do you read me?"

It was Vern Baumgartner. But his voice was on the threshold of inaudibility. I shook my head. It was still almost impossible to hear him. I checked my receiver. Somehow, while napping, I accidently had turned the volume control down. It was midnight. Vern was calling for the hourly report. One by one I checked the items on the list and read them off to him. The temperature had dropped while I slept, and the capsule was comfortable. No longer did I have to drag my every action through a veil of exhaustion.

A glance at the altimeter confirmed what I had seen before dropping off to sleep. I was at 75,000 feet now and still descending, slowly edging down toward the rising storm below. The thunderheads were beautiful, but I had no desire to see them from within. One of the first lessons even a novice light-plane pilot learns is profound respect for the violently churning, up-and-down wind currents in thunderstorms. In an airplane, controls are direct and effective, and one can steer clear of storms. But in a balloon, the only controls are up and down. I was still safely above the massive storm, but I could no longer consider it only as a thing of beauty to be studied. Each puffy, anvil-shaped finger above the storm was a thunderhead whose swirling stem contained natural forces as violent as the fiercest hurricane: winds that could dash my silent balloon about like a child's plaything, and electromagnetic forces whose slashing charges of lightning could turn the Man High capsule into an incinerator.

The balloon still was at least 15,000 feet above the storm. But I knew I must ballast. I could not continue the relentless descent.

"Three One," I called.

"Go ahead," Winzen replied sleepily. He had been on the radio or sitting beside it with Baumgartner, Archibald, and Stapp ever since I took off.

"I'm still descending slowly and I think I will have to ballast."

"Is your number 4 battery exhausted yet?"

"Just about, Otto. I'd rather not wait at any rate. This will be the last battery I can spare for ballast tonight and I think I'd better drop it now before I lose any more altitude."

"I agree, Dave. Good luck. Call as soon as it's away."

It was a touchy and delicate problem. For above me the polyethylene of the balloon had now cooled to 95 degrees below zero. It was as brittle as a thin sheet of glass. When I cut the 50-pound battery away, it would be like snapping a tense rubber band. The shock of the sudden loss of weight would race up the suspension lines to the brittle balloon above. Would the jolt be enough to break it?

Tense but still, lest I add to the shock by moving my own body, I reached for the ballast switch. And holding my breath, I flicked it. The capsule jerked sharply. It would take about four seconds for the shock to run up the lines to the balloon. I counted.

"One, mississippi . . . two, mississippi . . . three, mississippi . . . four, mississippi . . . it must be there."

My buttocks tensed, waiting for the precipitous feeling of falling that would surely come instantly if the balloon had burst. Four seconds later, the shock returned from the balloon. It had taken the jolt without breaking.

"N-C-A Three One. The battery is away. All's well."

"Good," Otto called. I could hear the relief in his voice, almost as if he had tensed up with me, waiting to fall from the sky.

"Otto," I called. "Why don't you try to get some sleep now. I feel better from my nap, and I know that none of you have slept at all. You and Colonel Stapp and Arch could take turns standing by."

"Don't worry about us, Dave," he called. "We'll nap when we're tired. Right now we are all keeping pretty busy watching this storm front and keeping track of you."

"Is the front still moving through okay?"

"That's one reason we're keeping an eye on it, Dave. It isn't sliding through as fast as Duke thought it would."

"Well, so long as I can stay way above it there's nothing to worry about. I can't judge very well looking straight down, but I'd guess I have at least 15,000 feet clearance."

There seemed to be no cause for alarm. My altimeter was dropping slightly, but I was confident it would level off soon. Nevertheless, the presence of the storm was not comforting. I wondered idly what tricks lightning could play from a huge storm front like the one below. While flying at high altitudes in jets, I had seen lightning shoot out horizontally from a thunderhead, and I thought I had seen it pop straight up on one occasion. Trailing down from my gondola now was a 300-foot radio antenna, an ideal lightning rod. If I got too close to the storm, lightning could reach up from the thunderheads and strike the antenna.

Checking my schedule, I turned eagerly to watch the moon rise, and soon I was fascinated by a wispy layer of clouds it illuminated. It was a last-quarter moon, shedding just enough light to cast a shadow in a thin gossamer layer of cloud that spun toward the east like a spider-web floor beneath me. The cloud layer was close and must have stretched out at an altitude of 70,000 feet, far higher than any meteorologist had ever seen such a cloud before. Without the rising moon casting a light behind it, I would not have seen the wispy layer either. The cloud had no connection with the thunderstorm far below. It existed alone, high above the earth, drifting gently along, too thin to be seen in the daytime, too high to be seen from most airplanes.

The moon itself looked brighter, perhaps, but otherwise it appeared the same as it would from the ground. Diligently I swept the outside mirror of my telescope back and forth, but even when the capsule held steady as a rock I could not find the moon in the eyepiece.

Night after night before the flight I had practiced finding the moon in the telescope and had done it again and again without difficulty. Now I could not find it at all. Sadly, I realized why. When viewed from below the atmosphere, the sky has an ever increasing glow as it approaches the moon. With the telescope on the ground I had simply found the glow, then zeroed in on the moon by following the glow to its center. But out of the atmosphere the moon had no air glow around it. It was a single bright spot in a black sky. I had no way of knowing when my acquisition mirror passed close to its image. I had been afraid this would happen.

Next I tried to aim the telescope at several groups of

double stars in the heavens, hoping to be able to see the separation between a close pair of stars orbiting so nearly around one another that they appear as a single star when viewed from the earth. But to do this, I needed to see the exact position of my image mirror outside the telescope, because it was this mirror, like a catcher's glove, that would have to capture the light of the stars. It was too dark to see the mirror from the window at my right shoulder. I flicked on a red beacon light at the top of the capsule, hoping it would illuminate the mirror. The capsule cast a shadow directly over the mirror and still I could not see it.

My new-found comfort and alertness was not long-lasting. For now I was cold, uncomfortably chilled as the rapidly dropping nighttime temperature of the gondola reached my clammy underwear and spread a layer of goose bumps on my flesh. After reading my 12:30 report into the radio, I huddled over in my seat and cat-napped.

I awoke with a start. Suddenly the inside of the capsule flashed with a bright light.

"My God, it's lightning," I cried.

Had it hit the antenna? Was there fire?

Outside I could see the active pulsations of lightning in the thunderheads below, and they looked menacingly closer than they had before. But still I had no way of knowing whether the thunderheads were 1000 feet or 15,000 feet away.

The flash was the color of lightning. But if it hit the gondola it would have left some evidence. Probably it would have started a fire. Where was it?

Quickly I checked the capsule. Nothing was out of order.

But how close would a bolt of lightning have to be to light the capsule so strongly? Surely no more than a few hundred feet. With that proximity, why had I heard no thunder? Perhaps the thinness of the atmosphere muffled it.

I checked my altimeter. Down almost to 70,000 feet now. I had dropped more than I thought, cutting into the comfortable margin of safety that had left me unconcerned by the storm before.

For the first time during the flight I was genuinely afraid. Could it be that the thunderheads rose higher than the 55,000-to-60,000 feet altitudes most meteorologists always had thought to be a storm's limit?

"Good God," I cried as another bright flash flooded the capsule with light.

Now I was verging on panic. If I was that close to the storm, and lightning had reached upwards twice to lash at me, sooner or later it would hit. My capsule had become a trap instead of an observatory. And there was nothing I could do but sit here and wait for the last crashing flash that would hit and leave fire or total destruction in its wake. I had no more available ballast to drop away so I could rise above the storm. I could cut into my live power reserves to drop ballast but that would offer only temporary respite. For without power, I would have to come down soon and I could not descend through the storm.

Forcibly, I calmed myself. Panicky thoughts of dire possibilities will get me nowhere. The first and most important thing I must do is determine my true altitude and try to figure out how much space remains between me and the storm.

As I studied the clouds below, the gondola flooded with light again.

I slumped back in my seat with relief.

If strength had remained, I would have laughed at this

colossal practical joke the Man High capsule was playing on me.

Looking at my watch, I noted that it had been exactly five minutes since the last flash. The first flash had come exactly five minutes before that. In another five minutes, the flash would come again.

Above my head an automatic camera had been rigged to fire a photoflash strobe light every five minutes throughout the flight in order to record the settings of all the dials on the control panel. Earlier in the evening I had noticed that it was not working and thought no more of it. But suddenly it had come to life. Moisture dripping from the capsule roof in the afternoon apparently had short-circuited it, and now the wires had dried and the flash was running again.

Another look at the altimeter told me I had leveled off at last. I was no longer dropping. And as a result the balloon was hanging stably, floating at a steady altitude without the agonizing rotation. Now I saw stars steadily and clearly in the telescope, but I had no reference point so I could not tell what stars I saw. The gorgeous view was scientifically worthless.

I turned my attention to the thin high-altitude cloud layer still illuminated by the moonlight in the east, and pressed my radio pedal to describe it to the people on the ground. Instead of the irritating piece of impersonal equipment it had been during the afternoon, the radio now had a charm and warmth I had not expected. I resented the interruptions it brought earlier in the day, but now I welcomed the friendly, soothing voices of friends on the ground. Although I had been mistaken, the shock of thinking I was in danger of being struck by lightning had left me shaken. I felt at last the full impact of being all alone, far removed from the reach of any helping hand save my own. It was comforting to talk, even if only to relay technical information, to Winzen, Stapp, and Archibald.

"The moon has risen fully now," I told them. "It's like a dead-white crescent against a black sky. There was a very faint yellowish tinge to it when it was rising, but now it is free of the horizon altogether and it's just white. Looking at the stars around it now. Seems remarkable, but they're all fully bright and undimmed, even the ones that are quite close to it."

"All of us wish we were with you to see it, too," Otto called. "It sounds beautiful."

"It is," I said, "but the whiteness of it reminds me that I'm cold. I think I'll slip into my 2-clo suit now."

"Roger, Dave. But remember to do it gently."

Winzen had coached me again and again in the months past on the need for gentle movement inside the capsule at night. Any sudden motions could become shattering shocks to the brittle balloon above.

Delicately, I worked into the cover-all-type thermal suit, one leg at a time, slowly and with deliberately measured movements. The thought of what might happen if I jerked suddenly was frightening. If the balloon burst, I would drop directly into the thunderhead below. Patiently I strained and wriggled very slowly to work the back of the suit up to my neck, then I shoved an arm into a sleeve. But the rough side of my pressure suit caught against the sleeve and my arm was stuck, halfway through. I pushed. I tugged. I strained. I bent forward and pushed again. What if the obstruction broke loose suddenly and my arm shot free, throwing me off balance? Would the shock break the balloon? I paused. Then I strained some more. Every motion sent a draft of cold air into the pressure suit, down

MAN HIGH

against my sweat-soaked underwear. The arm slid through, gently. Then the right arm caught. Again I strained and shoved. At last it, too, went through and I zipped the suit closed. This simple dressing operation had taken a half hour. I was exhausted.

Again I slept. But hardly had my eyes closed when I awakened with a start.

The gondola was plunging and spinning.

"Great God," I thought. "The bottom has fallen out!" I was plunging God knows how fast into a storm that would surely kill me.

"What happened? The balloon must have split."

As suddenly as the precipitous fall began, it stopped.

With the jerky motions of anxiety I turned to look at the altimeter. Just a shade under 70,000 feet. What's happening?

I tugged a Kleenex from a box at my side and nervously scrubbed a porthole to look quickly around me. To the southeast something was obscuring the stars, blotting them from my view. Shifting my eyes and straining, as if trying to make out the shadow of a man against an unlit window, I made out its shape. It was a thunderhead, reaching higher than I ever imagined a dense cloud could rise. It was every bit as high in the sky as I was.

Now I knew why the balloon had dropped so wildly. It had been caught in the downdraft of a puff of wind thrown up from one of the thunderheads below. If the cloud to the southeast was at my altitude, there probably were similar thunderheads very close beneath me.

All of the fear that had gripped me when the light flashed came back with a rush. Now there was no doubt about it. This was not a case of the capsule playing jokes with me in the night. I was sitting right on top of a massive storm.

"I'm trapped," I thought. "Another gust like that and I'll be sucked right into it."

Fear raced through me with the speed of nervous shock, like the chill that comes instantly with an icy blast of wind.

My antenna certainly was trailing within lightning range of the clouds. If lightning did not hit first, the treacherous winds of the thunderstorm could suck me down like a toy, to be slammed about unmercifully and then shattered by a fiery bolt of lightning.

"I've got to get hold of myself," I thought.

Urgently, I pressed the radio foot switch and called Winzen. Even the comforting sound of his voice would help. I explained my position carefully.

"Are you certain about the altitude?" he asked. "If you're at 70,000 feet I don't see how you could be so close to the thunderheads."

"I know no one has ever seen these things so high before, Otto, but they are here and I'm right on top of them. At least one of them extends even higher than my altitude. I'll have to cut away some ballast, even if it does cut my power reserves."

"You'd have to drop a hundred pounds to do any good at your altitude, Dave. That will be an enormous shock to the balloon. I don't know if it can take it."

"I don't like the idea any more than you do. But I have to do it," I quickly replied. "I'd rather take a chance on breaking the balloon and pray that it won't break than sit here and just wait for this storm to pull me down or hit me with lightning."

"Roger, Three Eight," Winzen called. He sounded every bit as frightened as I was.

Duke Gildenberg's storm, which I had not even suspected until I got up in the air and saw it, contained an unexpected surprise even for him. Meteorologists had never before observed thunderheads rising above 45,000 feet, although they suspected the stormy protrusions might rise to 55,000 or even 60,000 feet. Now, thanks to his decision to surpress his knowledge of this storm, I had become the first man to see thunderheads at 68,000–70,000 feet. I knew he would be excited by the discovery.

Only now was it beginning to dawn on me why Duke had been so testy the night before when he delivered his forecast. He must have known this massive storm existed, and I knew now that he must have decided to gamble on it. Despite the anxious moments it was causing me, and the real possibility that I might yet be torn asunder by the forces of the storm, I felt no anger over Duke's decision. If the odds had looked to me as good as they must have looked to him, I thought, I would have done the same thing. If we had postponed the flight, there was a strong chance that I never would have gotten off the ground. Furthermore, Duke had not counted on the balloon losing so much altitude. He thought it would float through the night above 85,000 feet, and so did I.

But now it was time to ballast. I tensed my body as I reached for the number 5 and number 6 ballast switches. They would drop two batteries, 100 pounds, and the shock to the brittle balloon would be twice as great as it had been with the 50-pound pack.

I pressed the switches firmly. The capsule jumped as the batteries fell away.

And I counted. One second. Two seconds. Three seconds. Four seconds. The shock had hit the balloon now. I was not falling. It had held up. Four seconds later the shock returned.

I watched as the altimeter showed a rapid gain in altitude. In two minutes the needle stopped climbing. The balloon had leveled off. I had climbed only a few hundred feet.

But at least my hazard was not increasing.

Night is a fleeting thing in space, even in space as near to the earth as this. I had watched the afterglow of sunset in the western sky well after ten o'clock. Now it was 4:30 in the morning and the east was growing lighter. A reddish glow made a short fuzzy band where the sun would come over the horizon soon, and above it a layer of aquamarine faded away in the deep blue-purple of space, a darkness still pock-marked with the steady, colored light of the stars. By five o'clock the intensity of the sunrise colors had doubled, but they appeared altogether different than the colors of late dusk I had seen from ceiling altitude the night before. The predawn colors made broader bands as they grew above the horizon, and the blue of the sky was not the same polished, almost luminescent blue I had seen the night before.

My edginess at being so close to the thunderheads below almost vanished as I sat entranced by the changing colors in the sky. For two hours now the balloon had drifted like wood on a clear, calm lake, holding steadily at one altitude without rotating one way or the other. I was working with the telescope when I felt a sudden twinge, then the capsule began to rotate rapidly. The altimeter needle fell off: 70 . . . 80 . . . 100 feet in a minute's time. The storm was just beneath me. Again I had been caught in a turbulent gust of wind from a thunderhead below. The urgency of fear returned. Then the descent stopped.

As the capsule leveled off I looked anxiously to the east. It would be a nip-and-tuck battle between the rising sun and the grasping storm. To drop more ballast now would cut my power reserve to the absolute danger point, giving me only six hours of emergency power before I would have to be on the ground and out of the capsule. But it already was obvious that I would need more than six hours. I still had to drift by the massive storm front. And after that, descent alone would take three hours. Like it or not, I had to sit it out, hoping for the sun to warm the balloon quickly and expand the gas so that it would lift me out of the thunderhead's violent reach.

Fervently as an apostle awaiting the Lord's return, I watched for the sun to peek over the horizon. Soon it announced its coming, more beautifully even than Gabriel's horn could do.

As I looked where the light of the sky was brightest, my eyes were caught by a brilliant green flash, a rarely seen phenomenon caused by the fact that blue-green rays of light bend slightly more than red rays and are therefore briefly visible slightly ahead of the sun's red rays as they bend across the curving earth. It was beautiful.

The flash lasted less than a second before it was overtaken by the visible red rim of the sun edging over the horizon.

With the warm and friendly glow of sunlight, the balloon began a slow but steady climb back to the earth's ceiling and I felt vastly relieved, as if the greatest threat I ever faced in life had just been removed. For the moment, at least, I was safe. Back to higher altitudes with the warm balloon, I would once again catch the slow five-mile-an-hour westward wind that had propelled me the day before.

Now I would drift across the top of the storm. Soon, I hoped, I would see its edge and drift beyond it.

After hearing my six-o'clock pilot report, Otto called back to tell me that the airport at Fargo, where the ground crew had spent the night, was shrouded in fog. He had only a vague idea of my location above and planned to send the C-47 up in an effort to find me. Then Stapp came on the radio.

"I hate to sound repetitious," he said, "but have you eaten yet?"

"No sir," I confessed.

"Well, do so now. I think you had better eat one of the canned flight rations."

I ate slowly: canned ham and eggs, sliced peaches, and a nut roll.

Exciting, even frightening as the night had been, the steady efforts to break through fatigue in order to make the same observations, the same capsule check-list readings, the same routine use of cameras and spot photometer, the same unfruitful manipulations of the telescope had become monotonous. Between cat naps during the night I had looked forward to morning when I would be awake and alert to observe once again the startling things around me. But with the lower altitude at which I floated at sunrise, the chance to observe was less than I wanted. Airplanes could fly almost this high. My view of sky and clouds from this altitude lacked the exciting newness of first discovery that I had felt the day before at 100,000 feet. I longed to soar back again into the black void.

The monotony drifted away slowly as I gulped cold ham and eggs and savored the canned peaches of my breakfast. It was relaxing and satisfying, and it was a change. But far more satisfying was the knowledge, confirmed by my altimeters, that I was returning to the ceiling, to space, to the place where on this day I knew I belonged.

Below me the clouds, which had brought such hair-raising uncertainty before sunrise, represented two things that I wanted to escape. They stood for danger and I wanted desperately to get away from them. But they also stood for earth; they were a part of it. I felt as if I no longer belonged to the earth on this morning. My identity was with the darkness above. As I ate, the sky around me and above me grew darker. I knew that I was returning to the altitudes I had visited the day before. It was right. That was where I belonged. I was separated now, emotionally as well as physically, from the earth.

But there were mundanities to remind me of earth and normalcy. As I half crouched in the gondola to make another contribution to Archibald's plastic bottle, I was seized with the same problem which had led to the end of my pressure-chamber test at Wright Field. Both functions would have to wait until I got back on the ground.

And the radio reminded me of my tie to the earth. Otto called just as I was stuffing the empty cans and crumpled wrappings of my breakfast into a plastic refuse bag.

"N-C-A Three Eight. The C-47 has had no luck in getting high enough to break through the cloud cover. We still don't know for sure where you are, so you're going to have to do some navigating for us. We want you to start making omnirange readings."

They wanted me to take radio direction fixes on Civil Airways radio beacons scattered at various points around the Dakotas and Nebraska. With definite direction fixes on two or more stations, the ground party could plot my exact position.

"Roger," I called, irritated by this new chore that would

wrest me from the delightful feeling of identification with space. As quickly as I could, I took bearings on three radio beacons and relayed the information to the van.

By 8:30 I had bounced back against the ceiling, slightly lower than I had been the day before. The balloon leveled off just a shade under 92,000 feet. And below me I could see the full extent of the cloud system that had been my close companion during the night. It extended as far as I could see to the north, the east, and the south, a sea of billowy waves dotted with high domes that marked the dissipating remnants of the thunderheads that had been so active during the night. But to the west, at last, there seemed to be an end to it. I still could not see the earth clearly, but I saw what looked like a huge dent in the clouds along the western horizon. As the balloon drifted toward it, the earth beyond the storm system became visible. It was the end of the dense layer of clouds. Now, I thought, there are no more dangers. I am secure and safe far above the earth.

By 9:10, just after my hourly pilot report, the balloon had drifted across the treacherous cloud bank. All that remained below me was a tremendous, westward-pointing tongue of ordinary clouds. Peering down over the southern edge, the clouds made a steep, overhanging shelf that looked like a sheer cliff of softly carved white limestone dropping away below. I flicked on my tape recorder to describe it:

"This cloud layer which terminates as an overhanging shelf is so solid it gives one a feeling of being in heaven, above the rest of the world where you can look down over the edge and see the poor, faltering mortals. It's a strange sensation: a quiet world, peaceful, bright and dark at the same time . . ."

175

Now I was truly separated from the earth, away from it, completely identified at last with space, a part of this wonderful new frontier.

I had been looking for this reaction, but now that it gripped me I did not realize that I was having my first noteworthy taste of the breakaway phenomenon. Later, after studying and analyzing it, I would recognize that it deceived me with its idyllic sensation of superiority, of being above everything. In truth, the breakaway represented a low point in my physical and mental capacity. Both mind and body had been sapped by the stresses of heat and cold, of isolation, of fatigue, and of fear. Breakaway, like the escapist retreats of a catatonic mental patient, represented a low ebb in which I no longer possessed the power to think creatively, to function as I should. Instead, my mind drifted into space, in a sense trying to escape something that was inescapable.

The feeling did not last long. Pressures which I could not ignore were building up. Even though I wanted to ignore them, the ground crew wouldn't let me. They were worried. The storm front whose end I already had described to the crew appeared far more massive from the ground than from my vantage point. From the command post at Fargo airport, the storm still seemed an ever present threat to my safety. Winzen and Colonel Stapp had been frustratingly directing the C-47 into the clouds in an effort to find me, but the enormous altitude of the cloud system was far too great for the old twin-engined plane to surpass. My omnirange readings had given them a rough idea of my location, but they still were uncertain. They were genuinely afraid that I was stuck above the clouds and would be unable to find a way down. I already had been aloft for twenty-four hours, and in the capsule itself almost a day and a half. If I stayed aloft too long, the chemicals, the oxygen, the battery power that were keeping me alive would wear inexorably away. The ground crew was afraid that I was trapped.

For myself, I did not yet share their concern. Although exhausted, I tried patiently to convince them that the storm threat had passed, that I could see the earth clearly. If only they would send the C-47 westward, far beyond the edge of the clouds, they would be able to see me in the clear, high above the lingering tongue of clouds that still covered their command post. But they were as exhausted as I. They were unconvinced that the danger had passed. Since I still did not know exactly where I was, I could not tell them precisely where to go or which way to look once they got there.

The capsule was beginning to warm again, 55 degrees and rising. I struggled out of the 2-clo suit, no longer fearful of shocking the balloon which had now been warmed by the sun. I knew the temperature in the capsule soon would begin rising to the almost unbearable levels of the day before, so I switched on the air blower. Despite the ground crew's concern, I was glad to remain aloft as long as I could. There was much left to do.

But by 9:50, Winzen's anxiety had begun to get through to me. Perhaps I should find a way to descend.

Looking below, I could see that the clouds in the tongue that separated me from the ground were not cumulonimbus, the dangerously active thunderheads I had dealt with during the night. They appeared to be thick, sheetlike stratus clouds, benign drifters containing nothing more dangerous than soft, powdery crystals of ice. The thunderheads had slipped away to the east, out of my way. If the ground crew wanted me to come down, I would come

177

down, I thought, right through the clouds. They were harmless.

"Hello Three One, this is Three Eight," I called. "I'm drifting right now over the tongue of cloud described to you. They are simple stratus clouds, Otto. No reason why I can't descend right through them."

"Three Eight, wait." Otto's voice was on the raw edge of alarm. "We still don't know where you are. You might be mistaken about the clouds. Our plot shows you still over the thunderheads."

"I tell you, I'm not," I called back. "I can see over the edge of this system and there are no clouds beneath the thick layer of stratus I can see. If you want me to come down, this is the quickest and the smoothest way."

There was a worried pause, then Winzen came on again.

"Listen closely, Dave. If you try passing through that layer of clouds you'll kill yourself."

"But I'm sure I can make it."

"There's not a chance," Otto said. "Even if there are no thunderheads beneath you, you'll never make it. There's a 90-mile-an-hour jet stream blowing east at 40,000 feet. You'll come down as far as that and then be swept right back into the middle of the thunderheads behind you."

He was right. I had thought in terms of a straight descent through the clouds below. But the jet stream would grab the balloon and sweep it to the east, directly into the thunderheads which I thought I had drifted safely past.

"Roger, Otto. I'd just as soon stay up here as long as I can anyway. But I'd like to go higher."

"I think you should try for a better altitude, Dave. If you can get a few thousand feet more you'll drift a little faster to the west. That will bring you out in the clear a lot sooner and then you can start on your way down."

"Roger, Three One. I'll drop 50 pounds of ballast now."

The battery I was preparing to drop still had power remaining, but it was near its end. From now on I would be on emergency power. That gave me exactly six hours before I would have to be on the ground. The time was 9:50. Unless I could find a way to save power by cutting off electric circuits, I would have to be on the ground by 3:50 in the afternoon. I smiled with satisfaction. That was about as far as I could safely afford to push the system anyway. My air-regeneration chemicals would be weakening by then. And the automatic cut-down timer on the balloon above me was set for 7 P.M. I had no desire to be aloft when it ran down.

The battery fell away and the balloon surged immediately upward: 93,000 . . . 94,000 . . . 95,000 feet. Then it settled, but again began to climb slowly, a few feet at a time. The added height gave me a better view of the ground beyond the tongue of clouds. Far to the west I saw a sweeping serpentine green slash in the plowed prairie land. It was the Missouri River.

By ten o'clock I had tired noticeably. Each time I picked up a camera or the photometer it was more of an effort. By 10:30, it was all I could do to force myself to make the readings for which I had been so anxious to stay aloft. The capsule was beginning to get hot again. I was lost. I was tired. My neck was rubbed raw by the rubber collar of the pressure suit. Both of my thighs ached painfully and my back still hurt from slumping for more than a day and a half in the net seat. Remembering my efficiency chart, I gave myself a lower grade than I had marked the morning before. During most of the first day and night I had graded myself 98 per cent efficient. When I was frightened I dropped it to 90. Now I set it at 94. I was too

MAN HIGH

tired to realize how laughably optimistic that grade was.

By 10:45, my almost total inefficiency was creating a grave problem. I was having massive trouble with simple omnirange bearings. After taking a bearing, I read the number of degrees of the heading to Baumgartner. Then I realized suddenly that I had read the bearing backwards. Aware of the mistake, I read it to him again, and again I read it backwards. Half finished with one reading, I tired and dozed off.

Fatigue, I thought. Nothing but fatigue.

Below me the tongue of cloud now was slipping away. It was clear enough to start descent soon.

"Three Eight," Otto replied. "Before you start let's have a full checkoff report. Colonel Stapp would like you to include your pulse and respiration."

"Roger," I replied. First things first, I thought. I timed my steady gasps for air. Unconcernedly, I tripped the radio foot switch.

"Respiration is 44," I said. I thought of it as slightly above normal. Nothing alarming.

In the van Captain Archibald leaped from the bunk in which he had been resting. Normal respiration is 12 to 16 a minute. As a doctor, I certainly should know that. Yet I passed off 44 per minute as though it was ordinary.

Archibald grabbed the microphone, appalled at my lack of concern.

"Three Eight," he called worriedly. "Roger on the respiration. Now give me the carbon dioxide level in the cabin."

I was not disturbed. But as I worked over the CO_2 analysis kit, my fogged mind caught the significance of Arch's disturbed query.

"CO_2 is 4 per cent," I reported.

"Recheck that CO_2 reading," Arch called.

Again I analyzed the carbon dioxide in my atmosphere. It was still 4 per cent. Something was seriously wrong with my air-regeneration system. Instead of absorbing the CO_2 I exhaled, it was sluggishly passing it on, allowing the percentage of the deadly gas to build up in the sealed cabin. Months later we discovered that the problem was not as serious as it seemed. But now, in the gondola, I was convinced that the most dire emergency of the flight was confronting me. In working out the atmosphere system previously, we had decided that 3 per cent CO_2 was the absolute maximum we could permit. Beyond that, we believed, would be poisonous. Now I had passed beyond the safe limit. This, I thought, must explain most of my bumbling sluggishness, not simply fatigue.

"Three Eight, this is Three One." It was Arch on the radio. "Listen closely. The colonel and I have decided it will be best, in view of the emergency, to take over control. From now on don't do anything without instructions from us. I repeat, don't do anything without instructions from us."

Up to now, as the pilot of the balloon, I had been in sole control and simply reported to them what I was doing. But the decisions of what to do and when were my own. Now, alarmed by the CO_2 level and my obvious inefficiency, they had taken command away from me. From now on the ground crew would pilot. I would contribute what I could, but I would be the instrument of their commands.

At eleven o'clock the first command came.

"We're still not sure it's safe, but you'd better begin your descent now. You may start valving. Begin with the valve open for ten minutes. Do you read me? Over."

"Roger," I called. "Start valving with a ten-minute valving period."

As I hit the valve switch, I tried to think of a solution to the CO_2 problem. What had happened was clear. During the night when the outside temperature dropped to minus 90 degrees, the absorbent anhydrous lithium hydroxide had cooled so much that it had lost its ability to work quickly. Now it was sluggishly absorbing only a portion of the CO_2 I exhaled, and the rest was backing up into the cabin. If the chemical warmed again, as it soon should, it might begin to function properly once more. But for the moment it was not working right. And its absorbent quality might be completely exhausted. Just as I decided to clamp on my faceplate and begin breathing pure oxygen from the emergency supply in the pressure suit, Archibald called.

"Hello, Three Eight. We think the best thing you can do is breathe pure oxygen from the pressure suit for a while. It should make you feel better. Try wearing the faceplate and breathing pure oxygen in ten-minute intervals."

I clamped on the faceplate and began to inhale deeply the fresh, pure oxygen. Slowly, as if awakening from a heavy sleep, my body and mind reacted to the stimulating gas.

But now other problems were building up rapidly. After ten minutes of valving, the balloon still floated gently westward at 95,000 feet. It had not budged downward. At 11:25 Winzen told me to open the valve for forty minutes. Still I drifted slowly along at 95,000 feet. Theoretically, the balloon should have been dropping at a rate of more than 400 feet per minute by now. But the theory was not working. It had not dropped so much as a foot.

Meanwhile the noontime sun mercilessly baked the

capsule. It was 82 degrees, hotter than it had been at its worse the day before. But I had to cut off my air cooler, because I needed all of the power I could save. Unless I fell by parachute, I knew I would not be on the ground by 3:50, the deadline for the emergency batteries. By cutting off all the circuits I could spare, I might extend the power reserve an hour or two.

But it felt beastly hot, particularly during the ten-minute periods when I sat bottled up behind the faceplate of the pressure helmet. The tightly closed suit and helmet made my body feel at least ten degress hotter than I felt with the faceplate open. My initiative had drained almost completely from the joint causes of heat, fatigue, and too much carbon dioxide.

By using the emergency oxygen, I was gulping and wasting twenty times the amount of the precious life-giving gas as I would require with the normal atmosphere system. I was afraid I might exhaust the supply prematurely if I did not start down soon.

At 12:45, after I had valved for more than fifty minutes, I looked out a porthole at a strip of polyethylene hung there so that I could tell by its motion if I was moving. It had remained calm as a rigid board all morning. But now it was fluttering slightly upwards. I must be dropping a little, I thought thankfully. But in less than five minutes, it stopped. I had dropped slightly, then risen again. The gas in the balloon was picking up just enough heat from the sun to overexpand, replacing gas lost in valving and causing the balloon to rise again. Until 1:30, the balloon continued to trace this frustrating stair-step pattern across the stratosphere, first dropping slightly, then rising, then dropping, then rising.

It was agonizing. Below me the ground showed clearly,

a dull greenish brown. The cloud barrier was completely gone, but still I was inexplicably cut off from earth, stranded in the stratosphere.

During the night and early morning I had felt real fear several times. Each time it had passed before building to a disastrous crescendo. But now I was skating very close to genuine panic. It is, after all, a very serious thing to be stuck nineteen miles above the earth without a way to get down.

The capsule that had provided me with security from this hostile realm for more than a day had now become a prison high in the sky, an enemy which had trapped me in an impossible situation.

If I were not a trained physician, I am certain that I would have panicked completely. But a knowledge of the causes of my fear gave me a good beginning toward meeting the problems sensibly.

Steady now, I thought. Take these problems one at a time. I feel panicky for good reason. That's one symptom of too much carbon dioxide. It's also a symptom of heat stress. I can lick the CO_2 by breathing oxygen from the mask. I'll have to put up with the heat because there's nothing I can do to get relief. I must relax and save my energy. I can live with this if I relax . . .

If everything else fails, I can always come down on the emergency parachute. But I don't have to go to that extreme yet. If I come in with a crash landing it'll discourage anyone from ever backing this kind of a space-research project again. I've got to ride it down to a normal landing if I can.

But around me in the gondola the sophisticated system we had designed to keep me aloft for twenty-four hours was inexorably grinding to the end of its task. It had done the job well, except for the CO_2 absorbent, but now everything was close to wearing out. The entire air-regeneration system, the CO_2 and moisture absorbents, would not last more than a few hours at most. The emergency battery pack was draining steadily and might not last much longer even though I was trying to conserve it. When that went, everything would cut off. I wondered if there would be enough power left to trigger the explosive bolts that held the top on the capsule when I hit the ground. I could become stuck inside a dead space capsule, dead or near death myself.

Everything depended on the power system operating just a little bit longer than it was supposed to.

By 1:40 I had dropped to 89,000 feet. I was coming down at last.

But the joy of descending was short lived. The balloon started to rise again, then drop, then rise. The stair-step pattern in the sky continued.

At 2:10 I asked for permission to turn off my radio receiver. I had to conserve power. From now on I was alone.

Now the balloon began a slow descent. I waited agonizing minutes to see if it would stop and rise as it had before. But the drop continued. I knew I had to establish a 400-foot-per-minute rate of descent in order to pass through the jet stream as quickly as possible when I reached it. If I was descending too slowly, I might hang in the strong easterly wind just long enough to be blown back into the thunderstorm. But if I descended much faster than 400 feet a minute, my speed would be so high by the time I reached the ground that the gondola would crash rather than land. Descent speed, I knew, doubles when a balloon passes through the tropopause.

Two-twenty now and still dropping. Good. It's up to 310 feet per minute. If I can steady off at 400 feet I'll land okay. My God. Capsule temperature is up to 84. At least 94 inside this faceplate. Much longer and I'll have a self-induced fever that could knock me out for good.

But my troubles were not over. Again and again the steady descent rate slowed. And again and again I pressed the valve switch to release more gas. My fingers now were tiring from pushing against the strong spring tension of the valve switch.

For an hour I continued valving, waiting, valving, waiting. Each time I valved the descent would increase, then it would drop again. By 3:30 I had descended only to 70,000 feet. But slowly the descent was creeping up toward the 400 feet a minute I had to have.

Too busy piloting now to worry about making more observations of the sky, I began to stow all the gear that I had used during the long flight.

Hate to be knocked out by loose equipment when I hit, I thought. Clamp the cameras down. Slip the spot photometer back into its rack. Tighten my shoulder harness and seat belt.

What's wrong here. It feels like my arm's burning up!

I looked quickly at my right arm. A bead of intense light was burning through the material of the pressure suit. It was from the telescope. Somehow during the descent, the telescope mirror had picked up the sun's image and was beaming it through the eyepiece directly down on my arm. Hurriedly, I turned the mirror away from the sun. A possibility which I had never considered had very nearly caused a fire and disaster just as success was almost at hand.

But success still was 50,000 feet away. And my descent rate was falling off again. Anxiously, I began an almost rhythmic valving, opening the valve for two minutes, closing it for five, opening it for two minutes, closing it for five. Now the descent rate crept close to 400 feet.

I'll anticipate it this time, I thought. When the descent rate reaches 400 feet I'll open the valve for another two minutes to keep it there. I won't let it drop off again.

The rate-of-descent needle touched 400 feet and I hit the switch. After two minutes I sat back to relax, confident that I would remain now at 400 feet per minute until I passed through the tropopause.

Then I watched in horrified fascination as the descent needle crept up: 800 . . . 900 . . . 1000 . . . 1200 . . . 1300 . . .

Good God, what's happened? I'm dropping like a rock. Even 800 feet a minute is a hard landing; 1300 feet is crash impact!

I had not realized that during my final self-satisfied two minutes of valving, the balloon was passing through the tropopause. Instead of leveling off at 400 so that my speed would double to 800 at the tropopause, I had hurried the descent, valved far too much gas, and my speed had tripled.

The fear of a bone-crushing landing passed through me with a shudder.

I had 200 pounds of disposable ballast, part of the emergency power supply, remaining. Balloon dynamics are such that at the speed I was dropping, 200 pounds of ballast was a drop in the bucket.

Despite the power drain, I called Winzen.

"Drop 100 pounds at about 4000 feet," he told me. "But save the rest until you're about 300 feet off the ground. We're leaving the command post now to track you down by helicopter."

187

I sat tensely. Landing still was more than 30,000 feet away, but already I could feel its shattering impact.

Then providentially, the descent rate slackened. Slowly the rate-of-descent needle fell back to 1000 feet a minute and steadied there. I sighed with relief. The landing would be hard, but not as jolting as I had thought.

I checked my watch. Time had slipped away from me during the urgent and fearsome descent. It was 5 P.M. The altimeter read 25,000 feet.

Thank heavens. I can decompress the cabin now. I can open a porthole and get some air . . . cool and fresh air.

Fumbling eagerly, I uncoupled the lug bolts on the porthole just in front of me, and it flopped open. The cold air which streamed in was like sunlight to a man who has spent his life in an airless dungeon. As if I had been shot with a powerful stimulant, I felt strength returning to my aching muscles. The terrific heat brought on by cutting off the air cooler and wearing the faceplate of my helmet had cut my mental and physical efficiency almost to nothing. Magically, the fresh air suddenly made me a whole man again. But still I had to keep the faceplate on. Not until I dropped below 12,000 feet could I get enough oxygen from the outside air to breathe it freely.

Below me now, through breaks in a low-hanging cloud layer, I could make out the perfectly-squared, forty-acre sections of cultivated farmland divided by a network of roads running north from Aberdeen, South Dakota.

At 4000 feet the balloon slipped through a filmy layer of clouds, tired wisps floating slowly above the earth. I hit the ballast switch and felt a snap as one of the emergency battery packs fell away. The balloon slowed. Three minutes. Three and a half minutes. I hit another ballast switch and the last 100 pounds dropped off. Now there was no power save one small battery that would trigger the switch to cut away the balloon and open the upper dome when I landed.

Below me was a softly plowed field. The stubble of a newly harvested crop of flax made a beardlike pattern on the ground.

It was rising toward me now. Faster. Faster.

I felt a heavy jolt as the undercarriage plumped sharply into the soft earth.

My hand, poised over the balloon-release switch, flew away from the switch with a shock. Groggily I shook myself. The balloon was dragging the gondola across the rough furrows. Fumbling, I reached the switch again and pulled it. The huge plastic bag, lightened immensely now without its space-capsule load, lifted away.

The capsule toppled on its side, but my safety straps held fast.

I was on the ground safe. Looking around inside my capsule, a reluctance to end the flight crept over me. Despite the frightening problems I had become such a part of the sky that now, once more bound to earth, I wished to be up again, far above this plowed field.

Slowly I tripped the switch that released the upper dome and crawled out of my space-armored capsule.

A warm sun, the smell of freshly harvested flax, the feel of soft loam beneath my feet. Nostalgia for the stratosphere left me. I was glad, now, to be back.

Less than 100 yards away, bent across the neck of an old field horse, came a farmer in faded blue overalls. Astride the horse with him was a youngster, his son.

Tugging off my helmet and the sweat-soaked nylon liner beneath it, I called:

"Hello! How are you today?" I could think of nothing more dramatic to say.

"Howdy," called the farmer in taciturn voice as he and the boy slid from the barebacked horse.

"Grab the reins, boy." He turned to his son.

The youngster held the horse's head down to keep him from shying at the sound and sight of an approaching helicopter. It was Winzen, with Colonel Stapp, Archibald, and Foster, dropping to a landing on the field.

"Look," cried the boy, excitedly, "There's a helicopter. I always wanted to see one of them."

The space capsule which had just returned from thirty-two hours and three minutes at the ceiling of the world lay unnoticed at his feet.

Chapter VI

I wriggled uncomfortably in the bucket seat of the Air Force C-47 that had come to Fargo to lift the Man High crew back to Minneapolis. The tender neck abrasion, rubbed raw by the rubber seal of the pressure suit, tingled with a steady irritation. My arms, my legs, my entire body ached with fatigue. But I could not put wakefulness down to find sleep. Numbly, I sifted through the momentous hours since I first climbed into the gondola—how many hours, how many days ago? At last the experiment had been conducted. The Air Force had mined gold far above the earth. Now it remained only to scrutinize in minute detail all of the data that the equipment and I had amassed. The gold Man High mined had to be processed so that we could explain and understand the things I had seen.

The hazards, the emotional stresses, the extraordinary discomfort and physical pain of the flight existed to me now as objects of study, not as reminiscences of an adventure. I had literally lived in space for a day and a half. What had it done to me? The cosmic ray plates on my arms and chest would have to be carefully developed, studied, and microscopically compared to my flesh to see where the heavy primary particles from space had struck and what damage they had done. What effect had the enormous stresses of the flight had on my energy, my alertness, my intellectual creativity during the flight? Had isolation and the monotonous repetition of routine tasks shared in chopping my personal efficiency to near incompetence? I recognized now that the efficiency chart I had marked optimistically during the flight was useless except that it proved my mind so inefficient under stress that it could not grade even itself efficiently. Perhaps we could find the key to my state of mind by studying other data: the sound of my voice and the frequency of fumbled thoughts, mumbled words on the tape recorder; my remarks to the ground crew, all of which had been tape-recorded in the van; the spontaneity of my remarks, and their frequency; the complexity of expressed ideas and actions. All of these things would have to be analyzed.

Film from the cameras which shot periodic pictures of the instrument panel would have to be developed and correlated with all of the scientific observations under which each observation was made. The tape recorder would yield more than the important clues to my own mental state. It included dozens of spot photometer readings, balloon stability measurements, and general observations on the weather and the heavens. These would have to be transcribed, separated, and organized according to the times and altitudes at which they were made. The physiological data the van recorded before the heart and respiration radio went out, and the analysis of my body juices preserved during the flight would have to be reduced to meaningful form so that my physical reactions to the anticipation, the excitement, and the great stresses of the flight could be made scientifically understandable. My photographs and movies of the high-altitude sky, the sunset and sunrise, the clouds below me, and the earth's delicately arched horizon would have to be developed and studied with care to confirm the things that I had seen and perhaps uncover unsuspected treasures that I had not noticed.

To process this raw ore would take all of us weeks. I was exhausted, but my urge to get on with the study was as goading as the conscience of an anxious lover late for a date. For the next hour, I relived the past forty-eight; and on the uncomfortable aluminum bucket seats beside me and across the aisle of the airplane, my equally exhausted colleagues slept. Once in Minneapolis, sleep caught up with me, too; the blissful, heavy slumber of total exhaustion.

Late the next day we gathered in the Winzen company's briefing room to await an evening press conference at which I was to describe the sensations of a day and a half in space. Duke Gildenberg, chastened but vastly relieved that his gamble with the weather had paid off, came into the room and motioned me aside.

For a moment I groped awkwardly to find the words to tell him that I understood why he took the risk and that I was glad he had taken it. If Duke had not been willing to gamble, there would have been no flight. The data we now had securely recorded on my tape machine and in our cameras simply would not exist. And the weather that was following in the wake of the vast storm front I had crossed was foreboding enough to tell all of us that there would have been no second chance. Duke's calculated risk had been a stroke of genius and I was grateful for it despite the anxious moments of the night above the storm.

"Dave," he said, glumly, "I hate to say this right now, but . . ."

"Let's not talk about that weather situation now, Duke," I interrupted. "I'm glad you did what you had to do, that's all. We can talk about it later."

"That's not what I'm talking about," he said ruefully. "This afternoon we tried to listen to your tape recorder comments from the flight."

"Has the typist started transcribing them?" I asked.

"No," he said. "Some of the tape cartridges you used are blank. There's nothing on them."

If I had been wired for an electrocardiograph at that moment, my heart rate would have raced off the paper.

"Which ones?" I cried.

"The backside of the second cartridge. I guess it covered part of the afternoon, from 1:30 to about three o'clock. There's another blank from 11 P.M. to two in the morning. And a lot of the stuff on the tapes you used yesterday morning is weak and spotty, as if the recorder was cutting on and off on you. It ends altogether right after noon. There's nothing on most of the last tape cartridge."

"Oh, no." I felt like cursing. Much of the balloon-stability data I had recorded as the towering polyethylene bag rose, fell, and turned during the night was missing. These were the vitally important observations we wanted for future astronomical balloon design. I had jotted some of the observations down on my note pad, but the bulk of them were lost forever to the vagaries of a simple pocket-sized tape recorder. And all of the excitement and stress of my last hours, fighting to come down out of the sky, was gone.

Fortunately, I had not relied completely on the tape recorder as a repository of data. Although I thought my Midgetape would work throughout the flight, I took the precaution of jotting most of the important observations on prepared data sheets and my note pad and of repeating many of them to the ground crew by radio. Loss of some of the tape recorder comments would make data processing difficult, but we still had a wealth of information.

If only we could begin deciphering it, I thought. I wanted to disband the press conference and begin immediately. But we would have to wait another day.

During the press conference there were a few questions about how I felt, what I had seen, but most of the reporters seemed content with the simple facts that I had gone up, set a record, noted the obvious fact that the stars do not twinkle above the atmosphere, and come down. I was pained at this demonstration that others were not so excited as I at the look and feeling of space.

"Was it a spiritual experience?" one of them asked.

"I have a deep regard for the steady, progressive march of mankind," I replied. "I consider myself extremely fortunate to be able to move a step forward in the gradual pushing back of the frontier of progress. My spiritual experience here was tantamount to that of a biologist looking in a microscope and discovering a new virus."

"You sound like a humanist," he called almost belligerently.

"In that sense I am," I said. "To me, this is God: to contribute to the progress of mankind."

From the back of the room, another reporter wisecracked:

"They've bottled everything else this guy has done this week. Might as well bottle his religion and have a look at that, too."

With that, the conference was over. But the ordeal was not. Miss Hugoniot would continue puncturing my fingers for blood samples for another five days, and Sergeant Knox would drain 20-cc. blood samples from my arm every morning for another three.

And the emotional ordeal was just beginning.

The next morning the Winzen company accountant met with our local Air Force contract officer, Lieutenant Alex Aven, who had worked tirelessly in the past to help Man High. Stapp and I sat in on the meeting. Its purpose: to explain to us that the $14,000 the company had put up to finance the remainder of *Man High II* was all gone. Now there was no money at all left to the project. Unless and until the Air Force got more funds, we could do nothing with all of the raw data I had compiled. It would have to remain locked on the magnetic tapes and on the data sheets until we could afford to buy the manpower and time needed to decipher it. It was frustratingly clear that until the limit on research spending was lifted, we would not be able to get at all of the results of my flight.

There was glory aplenty. When General Sam Anderson, commander of the Air Research and Development Command pinned on the Distinguished Flying Cross and told me of my promotion to lieutenant colonel later in the week I knew that the long hard struggle had been justified. But still there were no funds with which to complete our work. ARDC simply did not have research money to give to us. Gratifying as the D.F.C. was, I had not thought of my flight as a hero's adventure. It was compelling to me solely because of the chance it gave me, and the Air Force, to learn about a part of the sky in which no man had lingered before, but to which many men soon would go. Already I had begun to think in terms of another Man High flight, one that would take advantage of all we had learned from

mine to explore more thoroughly the upper atmosphere
and man's ability to work creatively in space.

For a month I worked over plans for the flight, even
though I knew there were no funds to carry it off. It would
take some kind of a miracle to stimulate enough high
government interest in scientific research to get Man High
back on the track. But in case there was a miracle, I wanted
to be ready.

On October 1, I left for Europe. The Air Force had
decided to send me to the annual meeting of the International Astronautical Federation in Barcelona to describe,
in a scientific paper, my experience on the Man High flight.
On October 4, there was excitement in the streets. Every-
where, people held newspapers bearing wide black headlines. Clusters of men and women talked excitedly on street
corners. I knew no French or Spanish. But the gist of what
had happened came through to me.

Russia had put a satellite called Sputnik into orbit
around the earth.

In town after town through France and Spain every
newspaper was covered with the news. An unexpected, almost unbelievable miracle was flashing on schedule across
the sky.

At Barcelona the Astronautical Federation, once widely
viewed as a crackpot league of international Buck Rogers
buffs, drew the attention of the world. The Russian
scientists who had come to read their highly competent
papers on satellite technology, smiled happily over their
achievement.

"You Americans have been first for so long," one of them
told me, "that you no longer realize the importance of being
first. It is unimportant that you claim your Vanguard
satellite may be better than ours. The important thing is

that ours is up there now going 'beep . . . beep . . . beep'
and yours has not been launched."

This was distressing confirmation of an international
fact all of us would have to learn to live with: from now on
scientific research was more than a quest for knowledge
to the Soviet Union; it was a political race for firsts. The
Russians clearly were ahead of us in rocket thrust and
rocket technology. They could orbit heavy payloads with
creditable accuracy. But the one area in which we were
fairly certain they did not excel was space medicine. If
attendance at a scientific lecture can be used as an index,
most of the delegates to the astronautics meeting recognized this lead. As many of them attended my report on
the *Man High II* flight as appeared for the Soviet confer-
ences on Sputnik.

I was sitting in my room at the Ritz Hotel in Barcelona,
idly watching a chugging procession of ancient Spanish
taxicabs come and go on the street below when a cable
that signaled the beginnings of my hoped-for miracle
arrived. It was from Brigadier General Don Flickinger,
chief of human-factors research in the Air Research and
Development Command in Baltimore. The cable ordered
me to report immediately after the Barcelona meeting to
ARDC headquarters for an urgent conference on future
plans to put a man in space.

At Baltimore, Flickinger had gathered the Air Force's
most knowledgeable space medicine researchers.

"How soon," he asked us, "can the U.S. put a man in
space?"

Flickinger, as qualified as anyone to give the answer,
worked with us as we reviewed the knowledge the United
States had gained so far in space medicine: Stapp's crushing accelerative forces on the rocket sled; Dr. Siegfried

Grathewohl's and Dr. Harold von Beckh's many experiments in human reactions to weightlessness; Dr. Hubertus Strughold's wide-ranging work in probable space-flight operations and living conditions; Dr. George Hauty's classic studies in isolation and monotony; Dr. Jim Henry's rocket-borne monkey flights; and dozens of other space medicine projects including Man High.

The implications of Flickinger's question were overwhelming. For the first time, the U.S. seriously was thinking about space as a realm worthy of man himself, not simply the one-shot subject of basic science curiosity as characterized by the basketball-sized Vanguard satellite.

But where did we stand in space medicine? Were we ready? We had learned so much, but too many questions remained unanswered. After fifty years of flight and three wars, the Air Force still was not quite certain what distinguishes a "tiger" from a "bunny," an aggressive combat aviator from a meek one. We had some ideas about the kind of man we must find. But all of us recognized that there will remain an element of doubt in selecting good men for difficult jobs until we have learned far more about man himself, until we have plumbed far deeper into his mind and physique. Some day, for example, I believe we will relate the pattern of the reticular formation within man's brain stem to his conscious and subconscious thoughts, his emotions and his physical reactions, truly linking the physical and mental man into a more or less predictable entity. Perhaps this sounds horrifying to a people steeped in the rational and variable control of individual actions, but I think we will be able to blueprint the physiological and psychological man, to predict with certainty how a given man will react to both the known and the unknown. We will be able to categorize men precisely, to define the limits of their endurance, their emotional capacities, even their totally subjective reactions in any known set of circumstances. But this sort of knowledge is many years, perhaps more than a century, away.

At ARDC we worked from the background of my own experiments beyond virtually all of the earth's atmosphere, and from a decade of research in space medicine by a handful of dedicated men from Air Force and Navy Schools of Aviation Medicine, from the aeromedical laboratories at Holloman and Wright-Patterson, and from other military and private laboratories around the U.S. and abroad. Our background was new and spotty in places, but we could predict with reasonable certainty the circumstances and the stresses of flight in space. To some extent we could describe a man's reactions.

We knew something of the innumerable mental pressures that will squeeze a man in space and leave him perplexed and frightened at times, aware that no amount of engineering skill on the ground can change the fact that he and he alone is the commander of his destiny and that the miracle of life within him and the miracle of technology protecting him can be utterly destroyed by a single instant of thoughtlessness, a single unforeseen hazard, or even more frightening, a single act of a subconscious mind which he cannot even recognize, much less control.

He will go where no man has gone before to build for him the odds of survival or failure. But he will know some of the physical hazards: the high-acceleration forces which will increase the weight of his body ten times as a powerful rocket drives him away from earth; the even more jarring G-forces that will drag heavily on every organ in his body when the space capsule slams back into the atmosphere; the invisible barrier of atmosphere around the earth that causes objects falling rapidly from space to burn with the brightness of a Bessemer furnace.

And he will know and perhaps fear the monotony of his tiny capsule and the boredom of his endless circling through the black void. It will not be the kind of monotony and boredom that is merely unpleasant, like the irritating monotone of formless thoughts and idle prattle at a cocktail party or the annoying monotony of a dull speech. It will be monotony and boredom that can kill him, and although he will know how and why, he will not know when it has reduced him to making a fatal mistake. After staring for hours at the same panel of instruments, he may happily smile as an hallucination dominates his mind and leads his eyes to see that which isn't and, worse, his brain to accept it. The instrument panel may seem to melt away like wax in the sun; tiny men may swing on the needles of his flight instruments; he may see hostile rocket ships attacking.

If these horrors disappear before he has destroyed himself, he may find himself growing angrier and angrier at the oppressiveness of repeating the same tests, the same instrument readings, the same control movements, and hearing the endless words of advice from calm and well-protected men in the comfort of a control center on the ground. If he has not been wisely selected and trained in advance, he may even become so annoyed that his mind will conceive its last clever thought, and he will have a final feeling of happiness and contentment because he has devised a method of ending the irritation of these voices from the ground and these repetitive functions in the air. He may contemplate a deliberate suicidal mistake. Before doing it, he might congratulate himself on the supreme triumph of his intellect over theirs, then happily set about trying to kill himself.

These are not the idle speculations of science fiction. They are based on true results of some of the experiments in isolation and monotony conducted in Air Force laboratories. For a man flying in space, all of these problems might easily manifest themselves in the form of fear. And there will be an intangible momentum to these fears. They will acquire more force as the flight nears its end than they had at its beginning. Like a horse player shooting for an eight-race parlay, a man will brace himself with far greater uncertainty and fear at the eighth race than the exhilarating second or third. As he waits for the end to begin, he will subconsciously feel that the odds are growing worse even though he may know they are growing better.

As we considered these and other problems of space flight—the design of a workable atmospheric system such as my own in Man High, the rocket thrusts available to us, the structure of a livable space capsule—the answer to Flickinger's question came clearly.

If the U.S. is prepared to take a great risk in recovering the man, we told him, a space pilot could be launched within a year.

But we knew the risk would be foolhardy. Too much yet remained to be learned about launching, orbital flight, and recovery before a man could be safely and profitably rocketed above the earth. If we tried such a flight on an immediate crash basis, it would have only marginal scientific value. It would be a propaganda stunt. And a failure would backfire horribly. We had to take more time.

None of us were quite sure even how to go about tracking and monitoring the space man from the ground, much

less how to pick the man who would take the first flight
into orbit.

With this in mind, General Flickinger called me aside.
"Plan for another balloon flight next year," he said. "I'll
get you the funds for it."

What he said next made my heart race with excitement.
Since it would be impossible to plan another Man High
flight without first studying the data we had gathered on
my own, Flickinger would find the necessary money to unlock the mine of data that was still tucked securely away
in the tape recorder and cameras of *Man High II*. We
would start that job immediately at Holloman Air Force
Base.

From now on, Man High was to be a prelude to space
flight in which the Air Force would gain experience for
what was soon to come as well as information about the
earth's wispy outer shell. Not only would we select a space
man, we would test him at the edge of the hostile void.
And we would test ourselves as well; for neither in a
balloon-borne capsule nor in an orbiting space ship does a
man stand a chance of survival without the constant
vigilance of his ground crew.

Kittinger's flight had proven to us the possibly disastrous
consequences of seemingly minor technical flaws in our
space cabin. And my flight had alerted us to the equally
disastrous possibilities inherent in man. I had been the last
to recognize the intellect-sapping influences of fatigue,
heat, and the awful isolation of space. In the next Man
High flight, it was imperative that we improve the flow of
physiological and psychological information from air to
ground.

Dr. Jim Henry, with whom I had begun my space
medicine career in the long-ago V-2 rocket flights of rhesus

monkeys, had just completed a brilliant synthesis of physiology, psychiatry, and psychology, coining a new term to cover these facets of space medicine: psychophysiology. It was a wedding of sciences based on a pressing need. In previous flights, and in previous laboratory experiments, we had taken both psychological and physiological readings. From the psychological tests, we learned the kinds of stress a man underwent, but seldom did we get an indication of their degree. From physiological tests, we learned how much stress a body was encountering, but not about its subtle side effects. By joining the two, fitting test results together to draw much broader conclusions, we could find out all that was happening inside a man during physical and mental stress.

But it would be of little value to the man far above the earth if he alone knew the results of the problems besetting him. A thorough trace of both his physical and mental conditions would have to be maintained on the ground and studied constantly by experts who could tell instantly when fatigue, or isolation, or heat, or carbon dioxide poisoning had dangerously whittled away the judgment or physical capacities of the man above.

The mission was broader, the urgency greater. Working with Doctor Henry and Doctor George Ruff I charted the information we had to have. From the system we needed a constant reading on the ground of cabin temperature, humidity, capsule pressure, balloon altitude, CO_2 percentage and oxygen pressure; from the man we needed a constant electrocardiogram, respiration rate, and measures of body temperature and skin resistance. This last measurement actually fell between the mental and the physical. As everyone who accidently has stuck a finger in a wall socket knows, the human body is a conductor of electricity.

Like all conductors, human skin has a precisely measurable resistance to electricity. But this resistance changes with the emotional state of a man. Resistance is normally low when a person is sleeping or at rest or undisturbed. It increases as he becomes alert or excited. So by constantly measuring this skin resistance with two electrodes, we could keep an eye on the alertness of our pilot. If it ran very high, we would know that he was alarmed; very low resistance would tell us that he was inattentive or resting.

To assess the pilot's mental state, Ruff worked out a better set of subjective tests for the man to give to himself than the efficiency chart I had kept on my own flight. The pilot would rate himself for personal comfort, for alertness, for drive or initiative, for tension, and for over-all efficiency. In addition, Ruff would call loaded questions to him from time to time. The pilot's answers would tell the psychiatrist much about his mental condition. In effect he would be undergoing a sort of psychoanalysis while floating twenty miles above the earth.

Another experiment that would be valuable for true space flight occurred to us at the same time Ruff and I were planning for the well-being of the pilot. Why not expand the ground crew into a well-rounded scientific panel? It seemed probable that the pilot we eventually ground through our selection program would not be a scientist himself. If he was a scientist he probably would be trained in only one field and his ability to make observations outside of his own specialty would be marginal.

But if we organized as a part of the ground crew a panel of experts in cosmic radiation, in high-altitude physics, in meteorology, in astrophysics, the pilot could act as the eyes and hands of other men, taking directions on their experiments by radio, passing his observations directly to the expert concerned, and taking more directions as each experiment progressed. He could give a constant trace of weather patterns and cloud formations to the meteorologist, take a wide range of sky-brightness readings for the high-altitude physicist, handle equipment for the cosmic ray expert, and look at the stars for the astrophysicist.

Proof of this concept in a Man High flight could be invaluable to the men planning the nation's first true man-in-space experiment. It was almost a foregone conclusion that the first Americans trained for orbital flight in space would be selected for their physical and mental resistance to stress rather than for scientific competence. Yet their presence in an orbiting satellite would be almost foolhardy if they were not equipped to make some contribution to science other than the mere fact of their presence in the vehicle. A panel of experts on the ground as tested by Man High, would add greatly to the value of an orbiting space test pilot.

Eagerly I sketched out plans for the panel. The psychiatrist would be Captain George Ruff. As aviation physiologist to look for the effects of stress and study them on the spot we chose Captain Eli Beeding, a physiologist who wanted to be a Man High pilot himself and who already had made a tremendous contribution to Stapp's sled program by subjecting himself to the incredible, crushing force of 82 Gs for a split second on the rocket sled. The expert on brightness of the upper-altitude sky would be Al Boileau, representing Dr. S. Q. Duntley who was working on an Air Force contract at the Scripps Institution of Oceanography. Representing Dr. Allen Hynek of the Smithsonian Astrophysical Observatory would be George Nielson, an astronomer and expert in telescope optics, who would conduct stability experiments with the balloon in the hope of designing a more sophisticated balloon-borne observatory. Duke Gildenberg of Holloman would be the meteorologist ready on the ground to quiz the pilot on the appearance of weather patterns from twenty miles up and to direct his attention toward suspected but unconfirmed phenomena such as the dust layers I had seen high above the earth. Dr. Herman Yagoda, one of the Air Force's leading specialists and a world authority in cosmic radiation, would advise the pilot on the techniques of handling his cosmic ray recording apparatus while aloft. And I would monitor the flight and the ground crew as project officer and as flight surgeon.

Drawing plans for the panel of experts was not difficult. But finding a pilot with sufficient grasp of the fundamentals of the sciences involved to perform for the experts would not be easy. We did not have time to send him to school, but in order to act as an extension of the experts' minds, he would have to have a wide understanding of at least the fundamentals of their sciences. And he would have to be in perfect condition, able to withstand tremendous physical stress and possibly frightful hazards for hours at a time. Even more important than his physical condition would be his motives for wanting to take the flight. If he was simply a tough man out to prove how tough he was, he would be less than worthless. He probably would succeed only in proving that he was not so tough after all. We were much less interested in finding a man who wanted to prove he could "take it" than in finding a man who sincerely wanted to go aloft to learn something of value to mankind.

The first candidates were Otto Winzen and an Air Force captain who was a crack physiologist. Both were eager to make the flight. Regrettably, both were disqualified: Winzen because he was a civilian, and the captain because of a minor physical defect that showed up on one of his preflight examinations.

Now General Flickinger suggested that we go all-out to organize a selection procedure the Air Force and the soon-to-be-established National Aeronautics and Space Administration could use as the model for selecting a true astronaut. Although the plans for Project Mercury, the first U.S. man-in-space program, had not yet been drawn, Man High was to be the laboratory in which the selection of the Mercury astronauts would be tested.

After the first two candidates were disqualified, I picked three Air Force captains and a first lieutenant as candidates: another aviation physiologist; an experienced parachute tester and psychologist from Wright Field; an aviation physiologist who had been studying problems of weightlessness; and a young Holloman jet pilot who had been trained in ceramics engineering but had a broad interest and understanding in many sciences including astronomy.

Each went through an exhaustive set of interviews with me, Ruff, and Dr. Ed Levy, another psychiatrist, to determine their motives and their emotional stability. Each also was given an arduous physical examination at the famed Lovelace Clinic in Albuquerque, New Mexico, in which they were subjected to virtually every physical and chemical test possible for a human being.

Next they went through the familiar claustrophobia test and a high-altitude pressure-chamber run such as Kittinger and I had taken the year before. At this stage, one fell out with claustrophobia.

The remaining three then went through a grueling week of testing under a series of great stresses at Wright Field. Among the tests were a series of high-G rides in a whirling centrifuge; an hour of slow parboiling in a heat box whose temperature was set at 155 degrees with 85 per cent humidity; a pressure breathing ordeal in which they had to draw pressurized air in measured drafts against a force that made them feel as if they were suffocating; and an icy ordeal in which they were asked, without foreknowledge, to shove their feet and ankles into a bucket of ice water and hold them there, despite the cold and pain, for seven minutes. During all of these tests, Dr. Charles L. Wilson, head of the stress lab, watched their electrocardiograms, pulse, and blood pressure.

As the three pilots moved through the testing program, the question of choosing one of them to take *Man High III* aloft seemed difficult. But the problem solved itself, unhappily and almost disastrously in the case of one man, Captain John D. Schock.

Just as Joe and I had been required to get a CAA balloonist's license, each of the three Man High candidates had to check out as a balloon pilot. Schock had completed all of his physical, psychological, and stress tests and had all but finished his balloon training by August 13, six days short of a full year after my flight. He looked like the logical candidate to make the third Man High ascent.

On August 13 Schock and Otto climbed into a Winzen Sky-Car gondola and took off on what was to be the captain's final training ascent. Winzen was his instructor. Gently, they drifted south toward Wisconsin, touching down for practice landings, ballasting, and rising again into the sky. Through the day the flight sailed smoothly, but by five o'clock in the afternoon it appeared that they would have to land to avoid a thunderstorm.

But as they began descending, vertical air currents caught the balloon and the pair had to ballast furiously to keep from dropping too fast. Time was running out. Lake Superior, with its bitter cold 40-degree water, was fast approaching. Then as they approached an ideal farm field landing site the balloon began to descend. Otto lifted the safety cover of the switch that would cut the gondola away from the balloon when it struck the ground. Inexplicably the release switch fired. The gondola dropped away and plunged 100 feet to the ground.

Luckily for both of them, a local resident had seen them ballasting, decided they must be in trouble and probably would crash. She called for an ambulance and the State Highway patrol. Within minutes after the gondola hit, the ambulance arrived and rushed Schock and Winzen to a hospital at Ashland, Wisconsin, only a mile away. Schock's throat was cut almost from ear to ear when his head slammed downward with the impact and his chin struck his seat. The deep cut barely missed severing his jugular vein and carotid arteries. For days his condition was critically uncertain. Winzen broke several ribs, shattered his right wrist, and cracked his right clavicle, and was in grave condition from shock. Both were through with ballooning for months to come. Happily, both recovered.

But now only two candidates remained, and it was not long before the field narrowed to one. The psychologist-parachutist had shown a tendency toward high-cholesterol blood level earlier. Now the condition cropped up again. Although he had been designated as the probable pilot, he had to be sidelined in alternate status, to fly only if the other pilot could not.

First Lieutenant Clifton McClure, a ceramics engineer whose intellect and energies had by now become totally devoted to Man High, would make the final ascent in the tight-fitting capsule. All of the pilot-candidates had been good, but McClure had moved through the selection program and training period with extraordinary skill and strength. In every test he had poked curiously into everything he saw, eager to learn and to practice for the experience ahead. Tall, muscular, and keenly alert, the dark-haired pilot was both intellectually and physically restless but at the same time showed an almost remarkable calm. Although he would push his mind at full bore when there was something to do, he would take every free chance he could to relax and conserve physical energy that might be needed later, deliberately, like a prudent man going to the bank to deposit his savings. McClure had been nicknamed "Demi" by the Tennessee doctor who delivered him as "the first Democrat born" on the night of Franklin Roosevelt's first election in 1932.

During one of his pressure-chamber tests in which we recorded all of the conversation between McClure and the control group outside, Demi flipped his radio switch during an idle period and said:

"I am not sleepy now, but if there is nothing to do and if you can't find anything for me to do, I'm going to try to take a nap. I'd like to have something to do if there is anything . . ." He was storing energy for what he knew would be a twenty-four-hour ordeal.

Again, a short while later, he called:

"Say, how about getting out that list on the spot photometer. Let's go through a trial run, even though it won't work. I want to try to start familiarizing myself with it, the dials and their function. How do you use it? What do you do? Is it hard to get down? Or hard to put back up? What are the knobs for?" His curiosity knew no bounds.

By the time McClure was selected, the Minnesota weather had begun to deteriorate. It was September and the northern winds were becoming tricky. Duke Gilden-berg predicted flatly that if *Man High III* was not launched by the end of September, we would be out of luck. But McClure had not yet finished his balloon flight training. He still had to make three ascents before he could qualify for the CAA balloonist's license he had to have.

Meanwhile, we had finished deciphering the data from my own flight and were feeding what we knew into our plans for *Man High III*. The pattern of cosmic ray impacts on my arms and chest had been as we expected. There was no serious lasting damage. There were many traces of cosmic particles on the film plates that had been strapped to me, but unfortunately prematurely graying hair that already existed in abundance on my body was impossible to distinguish from hair that had grayed after follicle damage from cosmic radiation. Anticipating better results with McClure, who had no gray hair on his body, we sent him to Brown University to Dr. Herman B. Chase, an expert in the effects of radiation damage to living organisms, for a careful preflight examination that would be matched against a similar examination after the flight to determine if any hair graying occurred.

From the results of my flight the Air Force also learned to have a far greater respect for the inherent dangers of fatigue and heat exhaustion. In studying what we thought had been a CO_2 emergency, so alarming at the time that the ground crew took control away from me, we learned that the build-up of carbon dioxide in the cabin was at best only a minor contributor to my strange behavior. Navy scientists and others studying the effects of CO_2 on men in a sealed environment such as a submarine, had found that CO_2 percentage in low-pressure atmospheres such as mine could go far higher without danger than it could at sea level. A carbon dioxide level of 4 per cent was virtually harmless for several hours. My inability to function effectively during the final morning of the *Man High II* flight was almost solely due to the physical stress produced by fatigue and the nearly intolerable heat of the day before. Twenty-four hours of total isolation also had done its bit to nibble away at my efficiency. The effects of these stresses would have to be watched closely during McClure's flight.

It was three weeks before McClure found fair weather to complete his balloon flight training. Even then he had to rush to Bismarck, North Dakota, with Winzen's operations chief, the late Lieutenant Commander Lee Lewis of *Stratolab* fame, to make one of the necessary three flights. Lewis, who had retired from the Navy and joined the Winzen company to continue his life's work in high-altitude research, flew as McClure's instructor. By September 28, Demi had finished his training. But only a few days remained under Duke's weather deadline.

On September 30, we trucked all of the equipment, launch crews, and scientists to Crosby for another launching from the open-pit iron mine. This time we decided to make final preparations at the scene rather than exhaust the pilot and endanger the capsule by making preflight preparations before moving to the mine.

But on October 1, an early flight looked impossible. Ground conditions were fine, but high-altitude winds had shifted in such a way that if launched into them, McClure would have landed far to the northeast in Hudson Bay, Canada. It would be impossible to track him that far or to recover him once we got there.

We decided to move the entire operation to New Mexico, where Gildenberg forecast the early morning winds would be so slight we could launch the towering balloon in the open, from one of the Holloman Air Force Base runways. Within two days the capsule and the only two big balloons we had for the flight were on their way by air to Holloman. On October 6, with everything on hand for the flight we drew plans for launching after dawn the next day.

Chapter VII

There was a gentle, chilling breeze drifting across the white sands behind Holloman Air Force Base as Gildenberg strolled with me to the headquarters building of the Aeromedical Lab. Above the brightly lit air base a serene sky opened completely to the darkness of night with no clouds to obscure the sparkling stars and quarter moon overhead. Duke smiled.

"I don't bet on forecasts any more, Dave. But tomorrow looks good enough to go ahead. This wind will die down in the night and we should have dead calm at dawn."

I chuckled at Duke's oblique reference to the miscast weather that almost snatched my flight out of the sky.

"I wouldn't bet on one, either," I laughed. "Let's go over to Building 1265 now. I'd like to take another look at everything before I go to bed."

After the exhausting ordeal of my flight a year before, we had wisely decided that it was foolish for all of us to work through the night of preparations when some of us knew we would have to remain awake through a long night of balloon tracking twenty-four hours later. We had split the project into work shifts. As flight surgeon I would have to remain alert throughout McClure's twenty-four-hour flight.

So tonight I would sleep while others prepared him and sealed him in the capsule.

Building 1265 at Holloman was a high-roofed cinder-block structure, built to allow room for handling some of the huge missiles that had been tested at the base. Its high roof gave us fifty feet of clearance in which to run a crane for assembling the capsule. Colonel Rufus Hessberg, new commander of the Aeromedical Lab, had his office there and was directing the Air Force side of this Man High flight, while my attention was turned entirely to McClure's health and to the scientific panel. Inside the building the Winzen company capsule crew was going over a preflight checkout with Lee Lewis, who was flight director for the company. Near Hessberg's office, Sergeant Dittmer and Captain Eli "Lack" Beeding were helping Demi into his pressure suit. I had given him a complete physical examination earlier. Everything was in order. I left for home and rest.

Back in 1265 McClure was sealed in the capsule by 1 A.M., when Beeding flushed the cabin atmosphere and pressurized it with the now familiar oxygen-nitrogen-helium mixture. At 6 A.M. I returned, just as the sun began to press its rim against the distant peaks of the Sacramento mountains. The delicate job of balloon inflation was just beginning on a runway a few miles from the big missile building. McClure and his capsule were ready and waiting when I arrived.

The runway, still eerily half-lit in the dawn calm, was filled with the strange sights and sounds of a launching.

"Watch how you walk around that balloon," Lee Lewis called through a megaphone to one of his crewmen. Then he added in a softer tone, as if to modify the harshness of his warning:

"We only have two of these things. Let's not grind holes in this one before it gets off the ground."

Lewis was one of the world's most experienced high-altitude balloonists. With Mal Ross he had pioneered the Navy's *Stratolab* program and had continued to work on it even after he retired from the Navy and joined Winzen. Lee was a gentle man, quiet and self-effacing. He never raised his voice except to be heard. And in emergencies such as he had faced often during the Navy balloon flights, he was a reservoir of calm and courage. Less than a year later he was to die, struck down by a plummeting block and tackle as he stood in an open balloon gondola during an indoor stress test. And at his funeral at Arlington National Cemetery, the chaplain would turn his eulogy on but a single virtue—love—for that is the kind of man Lee was.

As the crew worked on inflation, one of the plastic tubes leading into the balloon twisted. Precious minutes fled as the men worked to straighten it. By 9 A.M. the balloon was only half full and a gentle breeze had begun to tug upon it, flattening the windward side of the giant polyethylene bag like a huge sail. I turned to Duke:

"Still think we'll make it?"

"If they hurry," Duke said. "It's only about two or three miles an hour now, but a few gusts and we'll be in trouble."

I stepped into the communications van and picked up a microphone.

"You all right in there, Demi?"

"Yes, sir," McClure replied quickly. "It's a little hot, though."

"Don Foster just put some more dry ice on the top for you. You'll feel cooler in a few minutes. Don't worry about it, but we're trying to rush things a little out here. The balloon is sailing with a light breeze and we want to get moving before it gets any worse."

As I spoke, the worst already was beginning to happen. A gust of wind slapped against the flattened side of the balloon and shoved it rapidly to the concrete runway. The helium in the balloon strained upwards as the wind forced it down, and the wind was the winner. The balloon burst.

For a moment there was shocked silence. All of us stared in disbelief at the fluttering remnants of polyethylene collapsing on the runway. It was like watching death as all of us uttered, almost as if we had practiced saying it in unison:

"Oh, no!"

I realized, perhaps more acutely than any of the others, that this was our next-to-the-last chance. One balloon remained. Once we unrolled that and began to squirt helium into it, there would be no other chances. If anything happened to the last balloon, there would be no *Man High III*. We had neither the time nor the money to produce another. McClure had only one more chance to get off the ground.

By now, I thought sorrowfully, Demi must feel like a bride left thrice at the altar by a fickle lover. Nature, this great cosmic thing all science is striving so earnestly to penetrate and study, seemed to be just as earnestly moving its forces to thwart us at every attempted intrusion.

The truck that had trundled Demi and his capsule out to the runway now drove the load slowly back to the big loft building and we removed McClure from the space cabin which should have been aloft by now.

Then we turned once again to the routine job of gathering weather data that would tell us what to expect tomorrow. For only one more day it would the same. Dead calm at dawn. Light surface winds after sunrise. Unless we were caught by unexpected gusts, or were delayed until so late in the morning that surface winds again rose too high for us, the next and last launching attempt in the Man High series would be made between 6 A.M. and 8 A.M. the next day, October 8, 1958. Uttering fervent hopes that nothing would interfere with the schedule, not nature nor man nor a combination of the two, we disbanded, some to sleep through the day, others to begin getting ready for another night of preparations.

By nine o'clock that night I had left the hangar. But as I departed I saw the effects of sleeplessness on the faces around me. Many of the men had lain awake through most of the day, worriedly going over the possible sources of disaster that we would have to watch for on the morrow. Demi, finished with what he hoped would be his last lean steak dinner before the flight, was dressed quickly. By now the job of hooking up electrodes and thermistors that would take his skin resistance, body temperature, heart beat, respiration, and electrocardiogram, had become routine.

Before heaving himself into the mesh seat of the capsule, Demi turned to Colonel Hessberg.

"Doctor Hessberg," he said, his eyes sparkling, "I'm going to sit as quiet as a churchmouse in here just to make sure I don't bollox anything up. Please don't let anything go wrong on the outside." Laughing, he turned and climbed into the capsule.

Working smoothly, Beeding flushed the capsule atmosphere. And like a well-adjusted clock the technical check-off ran on, efficiently, thoroughly, routinely, timed by experience.

"What's your Item Seven—capsule pressure—read now, Mac?" Beeding called into the radio.

Inside the capsule, Demi McClure was breathing easily and peering through his narrow portholes at the brightly lighted scene around him. He wriggled slightly against the pliant nylon netting of the seat, then listened as Beeding called for a capsule-pressure reading.

Hunching forward, McClure turned sharply to the left to look at the pressure gauge. As he moved he felt his wrist brush against the emergency chest parachute which was hanging from a hook on the capsule wall before him. Then a soft, heavy pressure fell against his legs.

Behind the shadow of the oversize helmet that almost engulfed his face, McClure's cheeks whitened.

He gasped in disbelief.

In his lap and spilling down over his legs was a billowing white fabric that looked like a quilted blanket.

It was more than 100 yards of parachute nylon.

McClure's arm had brushed against the stay pins that held the parachute pack tightly closed. The pins had worked themselves loose with all the handling the chute had taken in shipment from Minnesota. As Demi's wrist touched the chute, the pins popped out.

It was 1:15 A.M.

No one outside of the capsule suspected McClure's problem. For the moment, he decided, he would say nothing about it.

Steadily, Beeding and the others went about their work.

One by one, Vern Baumgartner checked out the radio telemetry channels that would feed us information on McClure's physical condition and on the condition of the capsule. Lee Lewis watched Beeding as he worked, then stepped up to the side of the capsule and peered into one of the portholes. He could see that Demi was leaning forward, bending over something. But against the light reflected on the porthole and the shadow inside the capsule, he could not make out what McClure was doing.

Lack Beeding turned to his microphone.

"How are you feeling in there now, Mac?"

There was a long pause.

"Umn . . . Feeling fine, Lack."

"Getting too warm in there?"

"No. No, the temperature is holding fine."

Appalled by the accident, McClure bent forward to see if the chute cloth had been damaged when it popped from its pack.

This parachute was a special one, rigged with a double release system for high-altitude emergency. Although high-altitude bail-out was a last recourse, the parachute had an automatic release that would allow its wearer to free fall from any high altitude to 20,000 feet. There it would open automatically because its wearer most likely would be unconscious and unable to pull a rip cord. There was not another chute like it at Holloman.

As he studied the nylon in his lap, McClure thought of his alternatives. If he reported the accident, the capsule would have to be opened and the chute repacked. That would take hours and would certainly cancel any plans to launch this morning. If Man High III had to wait another day it probably would be canceled again by weather. Duke had forecast bad launching conditions after this morning.

On the other hand, McClure thought, he could attempt the incredibly difficult task of repacking the parachute within the confines of his capsule, and tell no one what had happened. Several months before he had watched with intent curiosity as an experienced parachute rigger packed the special chute. At each stage of the packing process McClure had questioned the rigger, asking how each step was done and why. He was sure he remembered everything he had seen.

"But I won't let them go through with the launching unless I'm positive the chute is packed as well as it could be done by a professional rigger," he told himself.

Slowly and with meticulous care, McClure carefully gathered the armfuls of nylon, gently folding them as he had seen the rigger do it. But no professional packer ever had done this. Instead of a fifty-foot rigging table on which to work, McClure had only his lap. As he worked, he described each stage of the process to his tape recorder.

"If anything happens, at least they'll have this record," he thought.

Frequently he placed his work gently in his lap and turned to answer routine checkout questions from Beeding outside.

At last the chute was folded. Now came the most difficult part of the packing.

He strained desperately to force the stubborn, springy material neatly into the parachute pack, then to fold over its sides. Muscles straining, he held the pack together and one by one fitted the stay pins into place. By 3:30 the job was finished.

McClure carefully inspected the finished pack. It had to be perfect.

But as he checked the two pins that worked on the automatic release, his heart sank. He had inserted them backwards.

Deliberately he told himself that there could be no compromise. Either the chute was repacked as well as it was

222

*when he got it or he would tell the control group outside
and call off the flight.*

*Already tired from the effort of closing the parachute
pack the first time, McClure popped it open again. Prayer-
fully, with grim purpose, oblivious of the pain his fingers
now felt as they strained against the rough material of
the pack, he repeated the closure. This time it was perfect.*

The time was 5 A.M.

I returned to the hangar just before the capsule and its
trail of support equipment were moved across the airfield
to the same idle runway we had used the day before. There,
under the glare of a bank of huge spotlights, the Winzen
launching crew waited. They had not yet unfurled the
balloon. Once they started, we were committed for good,
and we wanted one last checkout before beginning the
irreversible launching procedure.

"Everything all right in there, Demi?" I called to Mc-
Clure on the radio.

"Fine," he said. "Everything's fine."

Colonel Hessberg called to Lee Lewis.

"You all set, Lee?"

"Ready to go," Lee answered.

He looked at Duke, who nodded vigorously.

"Okay then," he called. "Let's start inflating."

The compressed helium whistled a high-pitched squeal
as it raced through the inflation hoses into the balloon.

Duke turned aside to talk to a newspaper reporter.

"What's the point of having so many parachutes?" the
man asked.

"There are only two," said Duke, "and they're there because he might need them."

"But with that big cargo chute over the capsule, he won't need a personal parachute, will he?"

"He might. We put two unmanned balloons up a couple of months ago. When they went through the jet stream, the high wind laid them over on their sides and both ripped open. The gas escaping from the burst balloons twisted the big parachute shroud lines and the whole works came down like a rock from 40,000 feet. McClure would be sorry as hell to be up there without a personal chute if that happened."

I called McClure on the radio.

"Inflation has started now, Demi. It's today or never. I hope you feel rested and ready to go."

"I'm ready," he called, "in more ways than one. How do the surface winds look from out there?"

"Better than yesterday," I replied. "We're in good shape until eight or eight thirty, but we can't afford to wait past then or we'll be in trouble again. It's six o'clock now. We should have you off within an hour if nothing goes wrong."

I felt the excited abdominal tingle of a gambler who has put everything on one spin of the wheel. The wheel was slowing now and it looked as if it might stop on our number. So far, everything seemed to be running perfectly.

Vern Baumgartner sat in the Winzen radio van, looking calmly at a bench loaded with receivers.

"All of your telemetry channels check out okay, Vern?" I wanted to be certain there would be no last-minute failures in the radio system that was feeding us Demi's physical condition.

"Not a hitch," he said. "Electrocardiograph and skin resistance have come through clear as a bell every time I've checked them."

I watched the sweeps of peaks and plateaus making their

seemingly endless graph-paper trace that corresponded to
the muscle contractions of McClure's heart. Beside the
EKG, on the same roll of paper, another automatic pen
tracing showed a steady line that marked McClure's skin
resistance.

"His skin resistance was low for a while," I muttered,
half clearly, "but it's coming up a little now. He must have
been pretty keyed up with anticipation at first. Now he's
getting used to the idea."

The balloon was rising ever higher as it filled with helium.
Walking over to the capsule, I noticed that the dry ice pack
placed on it during the night had evaporated away.

"Is it getting hot in there, Demi?" I called on the radio.

"Oh . . . maybe a little bit. It's not uncomfortable,
though. Feels fine."

I turned to Don Foster.

"Don't you think you should put on some more dry ice?
He's not uncomfortable, but it doesn't take long to get hot
in there."

"I don't think we need to on this flight, Dave," Foster
said. "You and Joe took off with dry ice, but we've painted
the capsule exterior flat white this time and it should be a
lot cooler than yours was. Besides, we're almost ready to
launch."

"It'll only take a minute," I said. "Maybe you should do
it just to be on the safe side."

"There isn't time, Dave. Don't worry. He won't need
it."

Lee Lewis trotted over from the tension scale to which
the towering balloon was attached. The scale that anchored
it showed how many pounds of lift the gas exerted as it
tugged the balloon upwards. The capsule-suspension lines
hung slackly between the scale and the gondola.

"Dave, the balloon is fully inflated," he said. "We're going to shift the load to the capsule now."

Carefully, the truck holding Demi and the capsule backed into position under the balloon. The line holding the balloon to the scale was released gently and the tension of the straining balloon shifted from the scale to the capsule, securely anchored to the bed of the truck. The truck moved slowly away, edging its load and the towering balloon down the runway, away from the inflation crew and equipment.

"Stand by for launch, Mac," Lack Beeding called into the van radio.

"Roger, Lack," Demi replied, then added excitedly: "I'm already on my way."

The capsule and balloon were airborne.

We watched as Demi rose perfectly straight overhead, climbing rapidly toward the stratosphere.

"What's your rate of ascent, Demi?" Lee Lewis called.

"One thousand feet per minute."

"That's too fast, Demi. Valve off for 30 seconds."

I turned to Colonel Hessberg.

"Let's call the panel of experts together and get started. The hard part is over."

One by one, the experts hopped into an Air Force bus that had been equipped with a loud-speaker. All of them could listen to radio conversations there, but when any one of the scientists wanted to talk to McClure he shifted to the communications van where an extra microphone was set aside for the panel. As a stand-by "conference room" in case the balloon moved away from us too fast, a C-47 airplane had been rigged with a long table at which there were two microphones and eight headsets.

Demi was our eyes, our ears, and our hands. His inquisitive mind and broad understanding of the fundamentals of all our sciences had equipped him to handle all of our experiments for us. He was eager to begin feeding us the data we wanted, and as we digested it he was prepared to extend the observations, to go in new directions that might occur to us. He could go far beyond the capabilities of a black box, an automatic system which must be landed, reset, and sent aloft again to accomplish any more than it is instructed to accomplish before it takes off the first time. In effect, all of us were sharing the same laboratory in space, six minds of differing technical bent, all using the same set of eyes and hands in the Man High capsule. And our eyes and hands in the capsule were equipped with a mind of their own; inquisitive, sensitive, alert for the chance to make original observations and to the necessity for protecting itself from the hazards of flying in space.

Demi's first report was radioed from 24,000 feet. One by one he ticked off the items, pausing briefly before relaying the three body temperature levels which he had to read. His cabin temperature reading came next: 89 degrees!

"That's hard to believe," said Beeding. He turned questioningly to Don Foster. "What's causing it?"

Checking his design charts, Foster belatedly noted that the temperature gauge had been incorrectly installed. The sensing element had been located in such a way that it could not give a true reading of the air temperature in the capsule.

Beeding turned back to his microphone.

"The sensing element of your temperature gauge is sitting right on top of the air-regeneration system instead of up high in the cabin, Demi. What we're getting here is the temperature of that regenerating equipment."

"Roger, Lack," McClure called. "That makes more sense."

In the science panel bus, the task force of experts sat patiently waiting their turns to use McClure for their experiments. Duke Gildenberg went to the radio van first.

"Demi, our altitude reading on you now is close to 35,000 feet. You should be passing through the tropopause in just a minute or so. Watch to see if the wind change tips the balloon when you enter it. There is no jet stream today, but the wind is moving about 50 miles an hour."

"Roger, Duke. I'm buttoning up for it now, just in case."

McClure had been instructed to tighten his shoulder and lap straps, buckle on his chest parachute, and be prepared, if necessary, to bail out. The wind probably was not strong enough to burst the balloon by itself, as it had done on the two unmanned flights earlier. But the minus-73-degree temperature could freeze it so that a light sheer wind might break the polyethylene. We did not want Demi to risk being unprepared for the emergency if it did come. The radio clicked.

"Duke. I could detect no tilting of the system. But the inflation tubes streamed out a little with the wind. I guess I'm passing through the tropopause okay."

At 90,000 feet, Demi called again.

"Colonel Simons. I see the most fantastic thing, the sky that you described. It's blacker than black, but it's saturated with blue like you said. I honestly can't describe it to you. I'm looking at it, but it seems more like I'm *feeling* it. It's literally indescribable."

I knew his feeling. I had felt the same thing. An intense, obsessive desire to describe something which has no parallel. The color of the sky at the atmosphere's end: inescapable, yet so elusive that you wonder if it is a color at all; an infinity so saturated with this color yet so low in intensity that you *feel* it, but wonder if your eyes really see it. It is as if your eyes register the color, but somewhere between retina and brain the nerve connection that will let you comprehend it is missing.

"Lieutenant McClure," Dr. Yagoda called at ten o'clock. "May I remind you to change the film plate on the cosmic ray experiment? I will call when it is time to change it again. I want to expose the first few plates for two hours apiece."

"Roger, sir," McClure replied. "I'm changing it now."

At 11:30, remembering my own failure to eat, I suggested to McClure that he pause for some food.

"Okay," he called. "I just realized I haven't had a bite since that steak last night. Tell the dietitian that the prospects of a tooth-paste-tube lunch are not too thrilling."

Beatrice Finkelstein, of the Air Force nutritional lab at Wright Field, had prepared Demi's food package as an experiment in space eating. All of his meals were packed in collapsible tubes, thoroughly creamed food which he had to squeeze out and swallow. It was not too appetizing, but in orbital space flights, where weightlessness will prevent normal plate-to-mouth eating, the tubed food will be a necessity. And it is far easier to stow away tightly rolled tooth-paste tubes than it is to get rid of opened tin cans and paper wrappings in a trunk-sized space cabin.

As McClure ate, the balloon leveled off at 99,700 feet and began moving rapidly to the northwest, too fast and over terrain too rough for us to follow in the bus and van. We transferred scientists and the command group to the C-47 and took off to drone through the sky beneath him.

Finished eating, McClure got back to work, this time as the eyes and hands of Al Boileau.

"Warm up your spot photometer," Boileau called.

For fifteen minutes, McClure carefully followed Boileau's directions, aiming the delicate, light-sensing instrument through the layers of diminishing brightness that climb from the earth's rim into the upper stratosphere and finally drop away entirely in the darkness of space. On his last report to Boileau, McClure sounded tired.

"I don't know why handling this photometer should be so tiring," he called, "but I really feel exhausted."

I was not surprised. The photometer is a heavy apparatus and shifting it from porthole to porthole to study the sky can be exhausting work.

For the next thirty minutes we busied ourselves trying to co-ordinate another experiment involving an Army antiaircraft missile firing at White Sands Proving Ground, which Demi could see clearly from his vantage point. In the airplane, we listened to the Army's launching crew read off its countdown. The missile was set to destroy a drone target at extremely high altitude not far from Demi's position. We were anxious to know how well he could see and record the event from above it. But by one o'clock the missile firing had been canceled.

"Mac," Beeding called, "it's time for your regular pilot report. Start giving us the readings."

McClure's voice sounded sluggish as he rambled through the instrument readings: oxygen quantity, capsule pressure, capsule temperature. The ill-set temperature gauge now read 118 degrees, as high as it would go.

"Tell him to give us his rectal temperature next," I called to Beeding.

Doctor Ruff, sitting beside me, frowned. As an outside expert he was not familiar with the Man High capsule system, but 118 degrees, even on a faulty gauge, sounded alarming.

"Rectal temperature: 101.4," McClure called.

"My God," cried Beeding turning from the microphone. He swung back to the mouthpiece:

"Recheck your rectal temperature," he called.

There was a momentary pause.

"It's 101.4."

Ruff turned to me.

"What do you think, Dave?"

"I'm scared," I said. "It could be a mild fever from some internal source. But there was no evidence of any physical problem when we examined him yesterday. If he's got a temperature problem in the capsule, the closeness of his partial-pressure suit could easily induce a fever. We need a positive check on his capsule temperature right away.

"Lack," I called, "tell him to take out the dry-bulb temperature-humidity kit and read the temperature off his mercury thermometer. Right away."

"Demi," Beeding called. "Get out the dry-bulb kit. It's under the food container. We need a positive reading on capsule temperature. And drink some water."

For three minutes we waited. Then McClure called:

"I can't get any water. It's supposed to come up through this water tube, but something must be wrong with the pump. I can't get a drop through it."

After a pause, he added:

"The temperature's 97 degrees. I repeat, 97 degrees."

"Oh, no," I cried. "He can't possibly survive that kind of heat for the rest of the day."

I picked up the microphone.

"Mac, sit back and relax. But don't try to do anything else. I don't want to alarm you, but you know as well as I do that the temperature is too high."

"Roger, Colonel," he called. "I find it tiring, but otherwise I'm okay. I don't think it's bad enough to worry about yet. I'll be okay."

I remembered myself at a much lower temperature, still cocky and confident and rating myself high on my efficiency chart. I was the last to know how totally exhausted I was, and how marginal my ability to act intelligently had become. Demi's voice was sluggish and he admitted he was tired. I knew from experience that he was far more exhausted than even he thought.

George Ruff looked at me.

"Dave, I'm supposed to be here to advise on stress. That boy's getting too much. In our heat experiments at Wright Field we usually stop when the body temperature starts to go up. As far as I'm concerned, that's the point of collapse. I think we should bring him down."

"I know we should bring him down," I said, "and right away, too. It's only one o'clock now. The capsule is going to get a lot hotter this afternoon if he stays up."

"Can't he tolerate the heat until dark?" asked Colonel Hessberg. "If he can stick it out through the day, he'll cool off at sundown and we can land him in the morning before the system starts to heat up again."

"If it was later in the day that might work. But sunset is still six hours away," I said. "And it will be a good three hours after the sun goes down before the capsule starts getting cooler. It takes that long. It was midnight before I cooled off on my flight."

Lee Lewis, who had faced severe temperature problems on one of his own flights, offered a suggestion.

"Why don't you ask him to try cooling his body with the air-regeneration blower. If he can keep cool by hosing the air around inside his suit, he might be able to stick it out until nighttime."

"That's worth trying," I said.

"Demi," Beeding called into the microphone. "Try cooling yourself off with the air hose from the regeneration system. It'll make you more comfortable."

Demi's reply was quick and discouraging.

"I'm afraid it won't," he called. "I just tried it and the air from the blower is even hotter than I am. I think a lot of this heat is coming from that system."

"Try your water pump again," Beeding said, limply.

"It's working now, Lack," replied Demi. "I'm drinking as much as I can hold."

"I know all of this sounds pretty bad," he went on, "but it's really not as uncomfortable as you think. I still feel okay and I'm sure I can make it until the sun goes down. I don't want to come down. Repeat. I don't want to come down."

Ruefully recalling Kittinger's crisp "Come and get me" when we called him down, I turned to Hessberg.

"Doctor, we'll have to abort the flight. We've got to get him down before that temperature gets too high."

"All right," said Hessberg.

"Wait," Ruff cautioned. "When a man is subjected to this kind of stress, you can't tell how he will react to disappointment. McClure says he doesn't want to come down. He apparently isn't aware yet how serious this problem really is. Or at least he isn't admitting it. If you alarm him now with a sense of urgency, an order to land, you might scare him into a condition of real panic. Is there any way you can start him down without scaring him half to death?"

"Tell him we only want him to descend to the tropopause," Duke suggested. "He'll understand that the capsule will cool off as it moves down and stirs up denser air."

"Everybody agreed?" Ruff asked.

"When we planned this flight," I said, "we decided never to take control from the pilot or countermand his judgment unless we were absolutely sure of what we are doing. We also agreed to be scrupulously honest with him and he with us. I don't suppose it's a violation of that agreement to ask him to come down to the tropopause without telling him that we *know* he will have to come all the way down. It is stretching it, though. But I agree."

"Lieutenant McClure," Hessberg called. "After considering the temperature problem, all of us agree that you should descend to the tropopause to cool off. Gildenberg tells me that the movement of air past the gondola will cool it."

There was a short pause, then Demi replied:

"Colonel, I know I've got a problem up here, but I don't think it's bad enough to do anything that drastic. I don't think I can get to a low enough altitude to do any good before sunset anyway. So I might just as well stay here and ride it out. I request permission to remain at altitude, sir."

Hessberg turned to me, then to Ruff. I shook my head.

"Permission denied," he called into the microphone. "We do not think it would be wise to wait until sunset."

"But sir," Demi called. "I have accomplished very little so far. There's an awful lot I can get done if I stay up here."

234

I picked up the microphone.

"Demi, you know this temperature problem as well as I do. You may not feel it, but with a rising body temperature and with that high capsule temperature, you're not going to be very efficient this afternoon anyway. So any observations you could make might be unreliable. You're better off spending the energy getting down a little bit where you can cool off."

There was no doubt that we would have to bring him all the way down. I had stopped even thinking in terms of accomplishing any more experiments during the flight.

From now on it was simply a question of whether we would recover him dead or alive. I was appalled at the thought of any more delay in beginning the descent. If we let too much time slip away, I knew, we might be faced with the prospect of an after-dark landing. In all of my balloon experience, we had never recovered a capsule immediately after landing when it came down during the night. There always was a time lapse of hours, sometimes days, while we searched for it.

In McClure's case, I knew he might be unconscious when he landed. He would be unable to help himself. If he came down at night utterly helpless he could not even open the capsule for cool air. He would continue to cook in that sealed cabin until someone opened it for him. That surely would kill him. We simply had to be there when he hit the ground.

Lee Lewis got on the radio to call valving instructions. He asked McClure to valve in repeated short bursts rather than in one long period because he feared that the balloon might start descending too rapidly, adding a crash landing to the emergency conditions Demi already faced.

But the balloon hardly descended at all. By 3 P.M., apparently beset with the same problem that had held me at altitude when I wanted to come down, he had dropped only a few thousand feet from his peak of 99,700.

"Give us your pilot report now. Don't worry about all of your body temperature readings. Just give us rectal temperature only. We'll keep tabs on you from that one," Beeding called.

Demi replied with his report.

"Rectal now reads 104.1."

His fever was rising steadily at about one degree an hour.

"George," I called to Ruff. "I'm really worried now. How long can he go before he loses consciousness?"

"I don't know, Dave. Maybe 106 under these conditions, maybe less."

"We will have to bring him down on the cargo chute if he passes out," I said. "But if we do that, he's going to hit hard."

I turned to Hessberg.

"I think we'd better instruct him to buckle his shoulder straps and safety belt and stow all of his gear. He might lose consciousness any time now. Even a gentle landing could hurt him pretty bad if he isn't strapped down."

Tightening the belts would put Demi's back firmly against the seat and cut down his air circulation even more. His fever probably would go higher as a result. But we couldn't take a chance of battering his face against the instrument panel when he hit the ground. I wondered if Demi would deduce our real intentions from the instructions.

At first he resisted. But then, apparently beginning to understand the desperate emergency for the first time, he complied, responding in a voice now slowed and thickened so that it was difficult to understand.

Lee asked him to valve again to speed the descent.

In the capsule, McClure tripped the valve switch, opening two big holes for gas to escape from the apex of the balloon. With each movement, he grunted and strained from the effort.

Hammering at his dimming consciousness was a feeling of urgency, an awareness that this was more than simple overheating which could be corrected, then forgotten. Reaching for the metal top of his radio transmitter, he drew his hand back in alarm. It was too hot to touch, hot enough to blister a finger.

Where was the heat coming from? Had the capsule insulation failed? Was the sun baking him like a standing rib roast in an oven?

With difficulty he forced himself to think back to the moment that the parachute spilled at his feet.

"Repacking the chute," he thought, "made me sweat too much. I turned out more body heat than this system is designed to take."

From that point on, he reasoned, the heat had worked in a vicious cycle. An excess of sweat had overburdened the potassium hydroxide in the air-regeneration system. Forced to take the overload of moisture, the chemical heated up like charcoal on an open burner, and the air blower circulated the heat in the capsule. Increased heat from the blower made more perspiration, again tripping the heat reaction in the chemical absorbent. Around and around went the ever hotter air, McClure thought, boosting itself and him to a higher temperature each time. In addition, the lack of a final dry ice cap before he took off probably aggravated the problem.

"Almost time for the four o'clock report," he thought. "Altitude 85,000 . . . Rectal temperature . . . . Unh . . . . 105.2!"

Now McClure began to realize that this was no descent to the tropopause to cool off. He had reached the fever limit of most adult humans. Beyond that could lie brain damage, then death.

"Maybe I've had it," he thought. Then, through dimming senses, he forced himself to think of what panic means. It had been a long time. He remembered the surf tumbling in on the South Carolina beach, foaming and rolling as he laid out on the breaking waves to ride them in to shore. With the other boys of his Scout troop, he moved north along the beach to find heavier surf and more thrills. And then he found himself far from shore, fighting an overpowering undertow.

Nearer to shore, two boys linked arms and waded out, gradually forming a weaving human chain to most of their distressed friends. But McClure was too far away and washing farther out. Fearfully, he flailed against the powerful rip tide trying to fight his way to the human chain. But it was useless. He relaxed. Then he swam at an angle to the current; resting, swimming, resting, swimming. Soon he was out of it and made his way in through the more benign surf farther down the beach.

He slumped under the tight restraint of his shoulder harness and relaxed. It was still a long way down. He would have to save what little energy he had for the moments when he would need it.

But even the motion of relaxing took its toll. McClure's vision flickered with unreal color. He felt as if he was viewing the scene around him through the walls of an aquarium.

In the old C-47 circling lazily far below the capsule, we anxiously considered a drastic solution.

"He simply can not remain conscious much longer if his

body gets any hotter," I said. "What's his descent rate now?"

"He's coming fine now, about 450 feet a minute," Lee said.

"Duke. Where will he land if we have to cut him loose from the capsule?"

Gildenberg studied his wind charts, then traced a line on a map of the Tularosa valley. McClure's flight had remained within the boundaries of the valley, edging first over the Sacramento mountains, then drifting west to the San Andreas range. Now he was beginning to drift east again as he descended.

"I'm afraid that he will hit right in the San Andreas'," said Duke. "That means he might impact anywhere from a mountain peak at 10,000 feet down to the level of the desert. It could be mighty rough."

We discussed the dangers of a parachute landing. The capsule would hit at a speed of about 20 miles an hour. That wouldn't be too bad since he was tied down and ready for the blow. But if he was unconscious, he would not be able to release the parachute from the capsule. It could billow with the ground wind and drag the capsule down the ragged side of a mountain. Even if the thin metal of the capsule did not crush and kill him, the potassium hydroxide and lithium hydroxide in the air-regeneration system might leak out, dripping over his body and burning it with caustic insistence. Lee Lewis and Mal Ross once crash-landed their Navy gondola and both were burned by the chemicals before they got out of the upended capsule.

Equally bad would be the problem of finding him. In the mountains, it could take hours, even days, to locate the capsule. And without assistance, McClure hardly stood a chance.

"Leave him under the balloon," Colonel Hessberg sighed. "We won't consider the parachute unless we're sure that he has passed out, and sure that we know where it will land."

Time for the five o'clock report. McClure shook his head, trying to clear his spotty vision. Opening his eyes, the capsule wall, the portholes, the instruments, everything seemed to be bathed in a limpid green sea. With effort he made his eyes focus on the body-temperature gauge. Clumsily he pressed his foot on the microphone switch.

"Rectal . . . unh . . . unh . . . now reads . . . 106.6 degrees."

McClure recognized that nature's most powerful force, heat, was steadily and surely killing him.

At 60,000 feet, he knew he had at least two hours to go.

With a powerful mental effort, he vowed that he would not give in.

Straining to rid his eyes of the blobs distorting his vision, he saw the gun-shaped spot photometer sway against its rack.

"Got to stow it on the floor," he thought.

Reaching out, his fingers grasped the instrument's handle. Then they trembled and opened. The spot photometer fell. Almost as if it had been aimed the tube-shaped lens of the instrument slid neatly between the radio foot switch and the floor. The switch was jammed.

"Can't you raise him?"

"No sir. I've been trying for five minutes. He hasn't answered any of my transmissions."

I looked at George Ruff.

"Do you think he's passed out?"

"It wouldn't be surprising. With a temperature of almost 107. I'm flabbergasted that he's stood up this long."

I checked McClure's heart rate. It was still just over 180, almost three times normal, far too high for a sustained ordeal. His respiration was 60, five times higher than that of a normal, relaxed man. But at least he was still alive.

"Where will he land if we cut him loose now, Duke?"

"Still in the mountains. I've been recalculating it every five minutes. He hasn't moved much."

"When did we get his last transmission?"

"Thirteen minutes ago," said Beeding.

"Check with the people in the van back at the base. If they haven't heard from him since then, we will have to cut him down. I don't want to do it if he's still conscious and in control. But if he's passed out, that means he doesn't have much reserve left. We'll have to get him down the fastest way we can."

Beeding called the van radio, listened for a reply, then turned to me.

"They say they heard him transmitting about five minutes ago. And according to them our transmissions have been pretty spotty for the last hour or so. It sounds like there might be something wrong with our transmitter or receiver instead of with him."

We had landed the C-47 near Truth or Consequences, New Mexico, and were operating our radios on a small generator which had not been working well. It seemed likely that our own radios, rather than Demi's, had cut the communications link. Rechecking his heart and respiration, I found both still at the same high levels. The fact that neither had changed markedly was another indication that McClure was still conscious.

"Okay," I said. "It looks like he's still conscious. If he is, he needs that balloon."

The balloon was now at 40,000 feet, just about to enter the tropopause. In the next 10,000 feet, it would double its speed downward. All of us strained to peer up at the shimmering disk of the balloon far above us. At 38,000 feet a black object fell away from the now visible capsule and after tumbling 100 feet stopped short under a billowing, small parachute.

Demi had dropped ballast to check the doubled descent speed.

Now we knew for certain that he was still conscious. And still in control.

Moreover, his mind was functioning at an extraordinary level for a man with a 107-degree fever. Most people would be in a coma, perhaps suffering hallucinations by now. Yet McClure had been able to read his rate of descent, decide that it was too fast, and trip a switch to release ballast.

Straining against an overwhelming desire to fall back and close his eyes, McClure read his descent gauge. After dropping one 50-pound battery it had slowed from 1000 feet to 900 feet per minute. He decided that was still too fast. Reaching for the row of ballast switches at his left, McClure pressed switch number 2. A muffled explosion sounded just below him. The explosive bolts holding the expendable battery to the landing frame had gone off all right. But there was no jerk to indicate that the battery had fallen away. Something had jammed it.

Again he pressed a ballast switch. This time nothing happened. Another switch and still nothing. One by one he pressed each of the fourteen ballast switches on the panel. Only the first one worked.

Slumping in the net seat, McClure methodically examined his plight.

"A landing at 900 feet per minute isn't bad," he thought. "But the rate of descent might increase and the switches don't work so I can't drop any more ballast before landing. The balloon might start dropping so fast that it comes apart. That might foul the cargo chute.

"Should I bail out? I know this chute will work.

"But will I? I'm already so weak that I'm not sure I can strap on the chest chute, get out of the capsule, and still have enough strength left to pull the rip cord."

Blinking, he looked out and saw the sky darkening. The sun was setting. He reached for the panel and switched on the capsule's flashing red beacon light.

"Better stay with the balloon," he thought. "Landing with a parachute is bad enough any time. I'm not sure I could make it in the dark."

"There goes his beacon light," Lee Lewis called exultantly. "He's still alive and thinking."

The light's visibility meant darkness was coming. Even so, each little clue of activity from the capsule was like a gift from heaven. It proved that Demi was still alert enough to control the balloon in the landing. The question was, would we be right there when he hit?

Demi still had much to do for a safe landing. Before hitting the ground he would have to shut off the air-regeneration system, closing its valves so that the caustic chemicals could not flow out and burn him. He would need to open a window for cool air. And as he hit he would need to trip the release switch that would cut the balloon away to prevent it from dragging or bouncing the capsule across the desert.

Shortly before the beacon light went on, George Ruff had

climbed out of the C-47 and into a tracking helicopter at Truth or Consequences. As the doctor most intimately acquainted with the effects of tremendous emergency stresses, we had decided he would be the best medical officer to have on the scene when the capsule struck. The rest of us stayed with the C-47 as it lifted away from Truth or Consequences and began tracking the descending balloon from 10,000 feet altitude.

"I think he's going to land well clear of the mountains," Duke called as he watched the blinking light on the capsule. "I hope to God the helicopter has him in sight and sticks with him."

McClure stared into the split mirror mounted outside the porthole at his left shoulder. Above, the balloon still picked up enough light from the setting sun to shimmer. But down below, dusk was wrapping the Holloman missile range in indistinct formlessness. He thought he saw the shadowy image of the Sacramento mountains directly below.

"Did I see mountains?" he thought. "Looked like it."

With effort he recalled his aerial maps of the Holloman area. The highest mountain noted on the charts was 12,000 feet.

At 21,000 feet, McClure stirred in his seat.

"Got to get ready," he thought.

Slowly, with the deliberation of a machine driving automatic arms to do one task at a time, he shut down the air-regeneration system, closing the valves which could leak caustic chemicals if the capsule crashed. With precision, he checked the electrical switches: radio, off; air blower, off; emergency batteries, on. He thought of something else.

"All future flights," he dictated into his tape recorder,

"should have some provision for dumping the liquid oxygen overboard before landing. It creates a fire hazard."

He sat back again, exhausted.

At 13,000 feet, McClure reached up to the instrument panel. Fumbling with the small panel light, he aimed it directly on the altimeter, bathing the rotating needle now dropping steadily to 12,900 . . . 12,800 . . . 12,700 . . .

He directed the beam of a second small panel light to play on two switches, each covered by a red, spring-held safety guard. Carefully he lifted the guards and eased two fingers over the switches beneath them. When the gondola struck the ground, he would pull the switches to release the balloon.

"If I'm out when I hit," he thought, *"the impact will jerk my fingers down over the switches to cut the balloon free."*

Weakly he sat and waited.

The altimeter spun on. 12,200 . . . 12,100 . . . 12,000 . . .

"Mountain level . . . might hit any time now," he thought.

11,000 . . .

10,000 . . .

9000 . . .

8000 . . .

"Floor of the desert is 4400 feet above sea level," McClure thought. *"Maybe I'll miss the mountains after all."*

6000 . . .

5000 . . .

4700 . . .

4500 . . .

WHAM! The capsule struck and tipped crazily to one side.

"Am I going over?"

It rocked back upright.

245

McClure's fingers tugged the release switches.

And the balloon drifted free, leaving the capsule standing upright on the desert sand.

Then there was silence.

Doctor Ruff rushed from the helicopter to the capsule, unsure of what he would find. He knew Demi was still alive, and thought he was conscious because he had cut the balloon loose.

As Ruff approached, the top hemisphere of the Man High capsule fell away. Demi had stood up in his seat and pushed it off. Then he stood there, looking out and smiling as his face felt the cool wind.

Helping him down, Ruff spoke soothingly.

"Lie down here. We'll have a stretcher in a second."

"A stretcher?" Demi raised his head. "I've come down almost 100,000 feet by myself. I can make the last few feet on my own, thanks."

He walked to the helicopter, clambered in, and stretched out on his back inside.

His body temperature was 108.5 degrees.

Chapter VIII

"Normally," said George Ruff, "when you have a stress such as the heat stress Demi had up there, the body compensates. Physically and psychologically it extracts what it can from its reserves. And for a while, a man under stress will actually be more alert, stronger, functioning at a higher level even though the stress is sapping him.

"But pretty soon he reaches a point where the reserves are exhausted, and there's a catastrophic collapse. The point is, you see, that when the stress starts working, the body begins to eat away at physiological and psychological reserves, and when the reserves are gone, that's the end of it."

It was the day after the flight. We were sitting around a conference table in Building 1265. Demi had just finished describing, in fine detail, the appearance of the sky, the ground, and the weather patterns he had seen. Except for a slight weakness in arms and legs, he showed no signs of his incredible fever of the day before. He was as energetic and animated as he ever had been.

Ruff continued.

"What I'm driving at is this: because of the accidental heat stress, this was a much more important experiment than it possibly could have been if it had gone off normally, routinely.

"I don't know of any heat experiment that has ever gone this high. Usually we stop as soon as the body temperature starts to rise. This is considered the point of collapse, and we know that most people can't go much farther. But Demi apparently has a practically inexhaustible reserve. I know that most people wouldn't have been able to tolerate this stress."

Duke Gildenberg tapped a pencil on the table and asked:

"Do you think the difference in atmosphere might have had something to do with it? The oxygen-rich atmosphere with helium?"

"I don't see any reason why it should," said Ruff. "The really interesting thing here is to look at the man's performance level during the stress. He had problems, sure. But where most of us would have been out like a light, he was still running at a very high level. He was still having original thoughts—creative thoughts—when his temperature was 108.5. His comment about making provisions in the future for dumping liquid oxygen, for instance, came at almost the very end of the flight. It was an original, creative thought, not just a simple observation. And he found the energy to act on it, to dictate the idea into his tape recorder.

"On the way down, he functioned very efficiently as the balloon pilot, dropping ballast and taking care of all the things he had to do. And his memory of these events is very clear.

"An hour after landing his fever dropped to 100 degrees.

"He actually had a surplus of energy. He didn't want to lie still when we got him back to the hospital last night. He wanted to be weighed. He wanted his EKG taken. He was full of surplus activity, and it showed that he still hadn't reached the end of his string.

"This took an amazing amount of physiological reserve. And from a psychiatrist's standpoint, it was incredible that he could come out of it and be able to say such things as 'I didn't get to see the stars,' and then sit down for ten minutes to give you a very logical analysis of why he couldn't see them.

"Now, the e's something priceless that this can teach us about our selection procedures for missions like this. We pick pilots to do the mission as it is planned. We need to pick them to do the mission as it isn't planned. That is, to respond to emergency stresses.

"The other pilots who have been on the list for Man High in the past looked like they could handle things very well. And we felt very positive about them. But I wonder if any of them would really have been able to tolerate this extreme emergency, to call up such an amazing amount of physiological reserve?"

I shook my head. From my own experience, I wondered if I could have tolerated the terrific capsule heat Demi had withstood. At 85 degrees during my own descent, my efficiency had dropped away to almost nothing from heat and fatigue. Both Kittinger and I had shown marked irritation and apathy when the heat had gone above 75 degrees during our claustrophobia tests. So had the other candidates for Man High. I wondered if any of us could have survived Demi's ordeal. Yet he had come through it with a surplus of energy despite a body fever that would have killed many men.

The lesson of this unexpected but priceless experiment was abundantly clear to all of us. An essential quality necessary to an astronaut would be stamina; not in a purely physical sense but in a psychophysiological sense: a combination of deep physical reserves plus the all-important emotional determination to use those reserves. In our selection program we tried to delve into motivation of the candidates, and we tested them almost mercilessly for pure physical potential, but we did not assess stamina, particularly psychic stamina, as a quality in itself.

Its profound importance was inescapable when we looked at the record of McClure's performance. Toward the end of his flight, after the spot photometer jammed under his radio switch, he was without communications, utterly alone at a completely hostile altitude under a physical stress that would have left most men insensible. Without communications he could get no help or comfort or encouraging words from the ground. He was completely on his own and he knew it. But instead of flipping into panic, his determination stiffened. He calmly set about relaxing to conserve what little energy remained. As we sat listening at the conference table, he told us how he relaxed:

". . . When I went to tune the transmitter or anything, I was real careful to be extremely slow, and I didn't try to do anything I knew I wouldn't have to do, and I would try to relax: to think that my feet would be relaxed, to relax my hands, tried to make my back feel the same way, and my neck, just tried to drop everything except what I needed. And still, I could feel my heart pounding all in the top of my head . . . you know what I mean, your heart no longer beats without you knowing it and your pulse is transmitted to the brain and it kind of hammers in the top of your head, and I was real hot."

By some miraculous accident, McClure had been dropped into the right place at the right time to be selected for Man High and events had moved inexorably toward this fantastic conclusion. During our first interview Demi had told me of his ambition to become a space pilot. I learned later that even before he heard of Man High, Demi was consciously preparing himself for such a challenge, purposefully aiming himself toward a recognized goal. To him it was no accident that he was ready.

A few months ago, while I was working on the beginnings of this book, Demi sent me a letter about his ambitions. Among other things, he wrote:

"There are quite a few things to talk to you about. One of these is my own idea of what I would like to accomplish while I live. Perhaps, by stating this, you will understand . . .

"The underlying thing is to do something with my life, to leave the world better because I was here. I don't necessarily expect that anything I do will be earth-shaking, but I want at least to accomplish something. In keeping with the thought that the most a man can accomplish is in areas where he is most interested, I would prefer to do a job connected with flight and science. The biggest dream, of course, lies in using the basic scientific tools in space to unlock some of the wonderful secrets that are held there.

"I know that the desire and singlemindedness to do this is paramount; however, this desire in itself may not insure that I will be allowed to take such a mission. In breaking down the steps to prepare myself, I therefore select less desirable tasks that wouldn't be in the running with space-flight, were I given a choice. In this way, I hope that the accomplishment of each of these allows some satisfaction of the original desire to do something, as well as making me better able to perform or more likely to be selected for the most desirable task . . .

". . . It has become obvious that my time for usefulness

will most likely occur with the second generation of space-craft. These will be required to be gliders, and therefore I intend to become proficient in glider flying. If at the same time that I practice, I can accomplish something scientifically, then even if I am not allowed to glide some day on re-entry, my training time will not be wasted.

"I firmly believe that in the space flight area the progress in the next 10 to 15 years will amaze the most optimistic person. I believe that people within one or two years of my own age will not only circle the earth freely in their ships, but will build a stepping-off, constantly-manned station and will not only circumnavigate the moon, but will land on it. I believe they will even make close approach flights to both Mars and Venus. I realize that I must concentrate and follow close lines to be a part of any of this, but in order to be of real use on such a flight, I want to study such things as petrography, geology, selenography, astrophysics, astronomy, etc. Imagine a metallurgist, ceramist, or petrographer on the moon's surface. Or imagine a person intimately familiar with the most violent storms the earth's atmosphere can produce, viewing the atmosphere of Venus from close range!"

These words from McClure eloquently illustrate the kind of motivation I believe is essential to any man who sets out to explore the space around us. There probably are many such men; men who want to "unlock some of the wonderful secrets that are held there." This is not the ambition of an adventurer, nor is it a measure or a gesture of patriotism. The goal is not to demonstrate our remarkable technology to the underdeveloped people of the world nor to run an extraterrestrial foot race with the Russians in a contest for cosmic records. It is, quite simply, to extend the frontiers of human knowledge. It is not the motive of a mercenary trying to prove himself, or of a neurotic trying to get away from himself. It is the pure motive of the discoverer, inspired by man's greatest quality, curiosity. In planning for space flight, we must look for men with these motives.

From McClure's experience, from Joe Kittinger's, and from my own we have moved a great deal closer to our ultimate goal. In two years, working on a bare minimum of funds and a maximum of personal effort by everyone involved in Man High, our simple Air Force balloon program reached far in the pursuit of knowledge and understanding. From the almost primitive notion of wondering what would happen if we replaced our high-altitude monkeys with men, we compounded our curiosity a hundredfold to ask questions about man which never had occurred to us until we got to the edge of space. Some of these questions we answered and thereby filled vitally important gaps of knowledge that the infant science of space medicine had to have before man could be expected to survive in space flight. Other questions we could not answer in our own experiments. But we at least could raise them, suggesting lines of research which might place the answers within the grasp of others.

From all that preceded the last flight and from the flight itself, we learned a lot about how to select an astronaut. We confirmed the obvious requirement that he be in top physical condition. We added to this the importance of deep psychophysiological stamina, an element which we ourselves overlooked until McClure demonstrated its importance. And we established a concept that should be fundamental to astronaut selection for all pioneering missions: that the men selected for a space research program must be devoted to research and not merely to their own survival. In the exploratory space missions this country undertakes, we should bend everything to the goal of learning all that we can about this new frontier. We cannot afford to undertake such flights for the sake of the blank accomplishment of being able to cry, "Look, we did it!" The men we send out away from the earth must have not only the initiative and stamina that will protect them from hazard, but the motivation that will lead them to the highest levels of human performance in exploring the strange realm around them.

Our experience with the Man High selection and training programs also taught us the importance of simulating actual flight situations as realistically as possible. One example of this was the standard twenty-four-hour confinement tests which all of us underwent. The results led us to an almost frightening conclusion. Although only two candidates in all of the Man High program were found to suffer from claustrophobia, their reactions led us to suspect that the problem may not always be so easy to find.

The first claustrophobia candidate, the alternate scientist who suffered a partial cardiovascular failure at the beginning of the project, demonstrated that a man's high motivation may so thoroughly mask his claustrophobia that it is not immediately apparent. It is possible that a man could consciously or subconsciously suppress claustrophobia and endure its anguish if he wanted badly enough to take the flight. In retrospect I have a mild suspicion that this may have been the case in my own first claustrophobia test. Pain from my long-healed knee operation, which had not bothered me for years, reached the point of near agony the first time I was bottled up inside the Man High capsule. Was this an outlet for a claustrophobic reaction, a not so subtle demand by my subconscious that I cry "uncle"? I don't know. At any rate it never seriously bothered me again. But if a pilot with a more intense claustrophobia had managed to get through the program on determination alone, would not his affliction have found an outlet if he had faced an ordeal as tough as McClure's? I am quite certain that his flight would end in disaster. Adding the massive stress of claustrophobia to the other stresses of such a flight would be asking more of a man than he could take. We are trying now to work out refined psychophysiological tests that will make claustrophobia more readily apparent. The reactions of a true claustrophobic irrevocably stuck in a six-foot capsule in orbit around the earth is a terrifying thing to contemplate.

From Man High, the Air Force also learned something of the effects of isolation, and confirmed to a small degree a theory of George Ruff's linking isolation trauma to motivation. All three of us were completely isolated far above the earth. Each of us faced one or more problems which could have been terrifying. Yet none of us actually became terrified. Kittinger confidently resurrected his old Morse-code training to overcome his communications problem; I gave myself a stern lecture on the importance of facing one problem at a time when fear began to overtake me during my flight; and McClure wisely made himself relax to conserve his waning strength. Each of us was motivated more by a desire to give our flight the appearance and reality of scientific success than we were by a fear that we might not live through the experience otherwise. Kittinger could have descended as soon as his radio went out, but didn't. I could have descended quickly on the cargo chute when my balloon refused to come down, but I didn't. McClure could have descended immediately when his capsule temperature passed 90, which he knew was beyond the limit of human tolerance. But he didn't. Had our motives been less strong,

I think all three of us would have succumbed to an intense desire to stop the flight and return to the company of people on the ground.

Isolation was working on us, to be sure. I felt it most notably in the breakaway experience on the second morning of my flight. When one reaches this state of indifference, a lack of mental discipline which permits a schizophrenic withdrawal from reality and the problems at hand, real hazard is not far away. But I snapped out of the breakaway reverie by giving myself things to do, things that I wanted to do and felt obliged to accomplish.

In studying the effects of isolation in his laboratory, Captain Ruff has found that persons of apparently low motivation showed much greater effects such as defensiveness and hostility than those whose expressed motives for taking the test appeared higher. Those who *wanted* to take the test for its value to Ruff as a scientist did better than those who submitted to hours of isolation in a soundproof box out of idle curiosity about themselves, or the desire to prove themselves superior.

In the area of monotony, we learned something from my flight. Both Kittinger and McClure were aloft too short a time and had too much to do to overcome their problems to become bored with the tasks they were performing. I never reached the point of actual boredom because I was too closely involved with the experiments I conducted, but the repetitive obligations of reading hourly and half-hourly pilot reports became irritatingly monotonous. And this feeling of monotony, just before breakfast, had made inroads on my efficiency. I have since tested this reaction to a far g eater degree at the Air Force School of Aviation Medicine where I am now assigned. I went through a simulated thirty-hour space flight in the school's space chamber. To test the effects of monotony, I concentrated on a single task, watching an instrument panel and manipulating controls to keep all of the instruments at a constant setting. During the last five hours of the run I had a steady stream of illusions and hallucinations: a helmeted soldier's face staring at me; a feeling that there were people perched around me; a feeling that all my surroundings except the instrument panel were as squiggly as a poorly tuned TV set. The obvious conclusion is that a man in an isolated space situation must be given a variety of tasks to perform. And, again, he must *want* to perform them.

One of the most important results of the Man High program was its gradual development of medical telemetry, the funneling of essential information about the physical condition of the pilot to the ground, and the interpretation of this information to tell us something of the pilot's mental state. Without the channels of medical information we received from McClure, he might well be dead today. He had to read his own body temperature and radio it to us, but from his heart rate alone we were able to follow his progress. Had McClure suddenly lost consciousness during the ordeal, our first indication probably would have been a change in his heart rate. We watched for such a change and were at least partially reassured that he was still conscious by noting that it was beating steadily at 180. It was through the medical information that we first learned of his trouble, not from the technical telemetry on the state of the capsule itself.

In various laboratories around the country other doctors are studying the effects of stresses as they appear singly on electrocardiographs, brain-wave charts, skin resistance traces and records of body temperature differences. We made an effort to integrate some of these measurements in order to get an accurate picture of our pilot as he flew. A far more sophisticated integration of such diagnostic elements is possible and will be developed before the space age gets much older. We will be able to look at a whole set of physiological and neurological measurements transmitted electronically and tell what the space pilot's psychophysiological condition is at any given moment. On McClure's flight we were able to correlate his seeming sluggishness, as expressed in radio conversation, with increased rectal temperature, increased pulse rate, and increased respiration rate. Except for the misplaced temperature gauge, which we knew was unreliable, all other information from the capsule indicated everything was fine. Without our medical monitoring system McClure could well have gone another hour or two at altitude before either we or he detected anything wrong. Had that happened, the flight would have ended unhappily.

There were many other positive results from the Man High program. By showing how much light was absorbed at various altitudes, our spot photometer readings gave upper atmosphere physicists new data with which to compute the amount and concentrations of dust floating high above the earth. Dr. Herman Yagoda gathered particles of nickel-bearing cosmic dust in a trap placed on McClure's capsule and was thereby able to give astrophysicists a close look at true micrometeorites, minute specks of cosmic matter which form vast clouds in space and rain down on the earth at the rate of thousands of tons a year. Although huge quantities of it reach the earth's surface, it is virtually impossible to distinguish from the earth's own debris unless it is trapped at very high altitudes.

In cosmic radiation, we confirmed the theories I originally set out to prove: principally that heavy primary radiation at the upper reaches of the atmosphere is not intense enough to be a hazard to a man exposed only a day or two. Farther out, we now know, the Van Allen radiation belts are a distinct hazard, but beneath them man can survive without serious effects.

Regrettably, we were not able to make full use of our panel of experts on McClure's flight, although all of us were thankful that the panel included George Ruff, an expert in exactly the kind of stress Demi underwent. Had the flight gone smoothly, the panel would have extracted valuable scientific information in other areas. Even in the short time the scientists did have, Boileau managed to get some usable sky-brightness readings. And Duke Gildenberg got a description from Demi of a cloud system over Mexico that was unreported on any U.S. weather map.

Looking to the future, one of the most pressing, perhaps the most urgent of the new questions for science which grew out of Man High is the clear need for an electronic system that will measure a man's capabilities in readily understandable numerical terms. It should be possible to devise something that will test all of the outputs of a man in space and of his confining space vehicle and give a quick and clear reading of his physical and mental state.

The main reason for putting man into space instead of merely sending instruments there is his distinctive capability for judgment, imagination, and creativity. But we have found that these unique abilities can fail, just as a box of instruments can fail. An engineer designing an instrument that must operate remotely always designs what he calls "back-up" systems, alternate instruments which either correct the failure or take over when the original instrument breaks down. In effect, we must design a "back-up" system for man; not simply an emergency device that will save his life, but an electronic psychophysiologist that will help save his initiative, his judgment, his creativity, and his imagination.

We know that when a man begins to run down, as I did on *Man High II*, his higher mental abilities such as creativity wane first, then deterioration progressively saps his ability to solve basic problems. Finally he is unable even to serve as a mechanistic link in a man-machine system, to read instruments or move controls.

We must learn to measure all of these abilities—literally to peg a man's creative ability at any given moment on a scale reading from 1 to 10—and then give meaning to the measurement by discovering how many notches down on the scale a given amount of fatigue, or heat, or isolation, or weightlessness, or monotony will bring it. These elements then must be correlated with the psychophysiological factors which we already can measure. All of them then can be fed into an electronic computer which will be the "back up", the guardian and watchdog of the man in space.

Picture a man making the first trip to the moon. He is alone. Instead of taped-down thermistors and electrodes and trailing wires, he wears a variety of peanut-sized medical transmitters attached to the parts of his body which yield meaningful physiological data. His head is dotted with a series of these tiny electronic tablets to transmit brain waves. Others on his body transmit heart function, respiration, blood pressure, skin resistance, and body temperatures. Each unit is independent, but all are powered externally by a weak electromagnetic field which radiates around him with enough energy to power the microminiaturized circuits of the transmitter tablets.

A receiver within the capsule picks up the whispered signals of the peanut-sized units, amplifies them, and feeds them into a tape recorder and into a computer within the space ship. The computer, set to understand the numerical values of each physiological, neurological, and mechanical element, digests everything and tells the astronaut where he stands. Dangerous combinations of psychophysiological symptoms and mechanical problems in the space ship will be detected automatically in their earliest stages by the computer.

Consider the moon voyager after many hours alone, assailed by fatigue, by isolation, by monotony. He will know that the inroads of these conditions are too subtle for him to realize. He will be in the distressing position of having to decide whether the things he sees and feels are reality or hallucinations induced by the stresses to which he has been subjected. He will know that illusions and hallucinations are possible, but how will he know when they have taken hold of him?

His psychophysiological "back up" will tell him. When hallucinations approach, the computer will detect the symptoms and unmistakably tell the astronaut to transfer control to his autopilot and get some sleep to regenerate his depleted reserves. It also will be equipped to tell him what to do to diminish the effects of monotony, or how to offset his feeling of isolation. With this ever vigilant overseer, the astronaut will be able to make even better use of his own uniquely human capabilities than he would be in a normal situation on the ground.

Such a capability may not be far away. Captain Ray Ware at the Air Force School of Aviation Medicine, and others at the school already have begun to explore and actively work on this kind of medical instrumentation.

Why do we set such difficult goals? Or more to the point, why did three of us risk our necks to learn the far less exotic things we gathered from Man High? The answer, quite simply, is that the very act of taking these risks meant that we were taking a short step forward toward the next difficult step and the next one after that to the seemingly impossible.

Hundreds more men, sober, largely unadventurous scientists are eager to take even greater risks, to push out into true space heading God knows where to learn God knows what. Demi McClure gave their reason as well as any man can when he said he wanted to use "scientific tools in space to unlock some of the wonderful secrets that are held there."

What are some of these wonderful secrets? I don't know, any more than I knew in 1956 what subtle things fatigue and isolation and heat can do to a man suspended at the edge of space. The comparison may be tired from overuse, but what did Columbus know of the wonderful secrets that lay west of the Atlantic void when he set out to sail westward to Asia? He knew he was trespassing an unadventured sea, pushing back a frontier that had confined the Mediterranean and European peoples for thousands of years. But he never dreamed what he would find, and even when he found it he had to make repeated visits to define it, and much time had to pass before the new continent was understood.

The great challenge of our time remains essentially the same: discovery and an unrelenting search for truth. And our goal remains the same as the utopian goal Francis Bacon ascribed to his mythical super race in the New Atlantis:

"The End . . . is the Knowledge of Causes and secret motions of things; and the enlarging of the bounds of human empire, to the effecting of all things possible."